D1083303

LECTURES ON FORMS IN MANY VARIABLES

MATHEMATICS LECTURE NOTE SERIES

E. Artin and J. Tate	CLASS FIELD THEORY
Michael Atiyah	K-THEORY
Hyman Bass	ALGEBRAIC K-THEORY
Raoul Bott	LECTURES ON K(X)
Paul J. Cohen	SET THEORY AND THE CONTINUUM HYPOTHESIS
Walter Feit	CHARACTERS OF FINITE GROUPS
Marvin J. Greenberg	LECTURES ON ALGEBRAIC TOPOLOGY
Marvin J. Greenberg	LECTURES ON FORMS IN MANY VARIABLES
Robin Hartshorne	FOUNDATIONS OF PROJECTIVE GEOMETRY
Irving Kaplansky	RINGS OF OPERATORS
K. Kapp and H. Schneider	COMPLETELY O-SIMPLE SEMIGROUPS
Serge Lang	ALGEBRAIC FUNCTIONS
Serge Lang	RAPPORT SUR LA COHOMOLOGIE DES GROUPES
I. G. Macdonald	ALGEBRAIC GEOMETRY: INTRODUCTION TO SCHEMES
George Mackey	INDUCED REPRESENTATIONS OF GROUPS AND QUANTUM MECHANICS
Andrew Ogg	MODULAR FORMS AND DIRICHLET SERIES
Richard Palais	FOUNDATIONS OF GLOBAL NON-LINEAR ANALYSIS
William Parry	ENTROPY AND GENERATORS IN ERGODIC THEORY
Donald Passman	PERMUTATION GROUPS
Walter Rudin	FUNCTION THEORY IN POLYDISCS

Jean-Pierre Serre	ABELIAN *l*-ADIC REPRESENTATIONS AND ELLIPTIC CURVES
Jean-Pierre Serre	ALGEBRES DE LIE SEMI-SIMPLES COMPLEXES
Jean-Pierre Serre	LIE ALGEBRAS AND LIE GROUPS

LECTURES ON FORMS IN MANY VARIABLES

MARVIN J. GREENBERG

University of California, Santa Cruz

W. A. BENJAMIN, INC.

New York 1969 Amsterdam

LECTURES ON FORMS IN MANY VARIABLES

Library of Congress Catalog Number 68-59230
Manufactured in the United States of America
12345K2109

*The manuscript was put into production November, 1968;
this volume was published on January 2, 1969*

**W. A. BENJAMIN, INC.
New York, New York 10016**

A Note from the Publisher

This volume was printed directly from a typescript prepared by the author, who takes full responsibility for its content and appearance. The Publisher has not performed his usual functions of reviewing, editing, typesetting, and proofreading the material prior to publication.

The Publisher fully endorses this informal and quick method of publishing lecture notes at a moderate price, and he wishes to thank the author for preparing the material for publication.

Dedicated to Rose and Nathan

PREFACE

The oldest problem in Algebra is solving polynomial equations. This book deals with a discovery made in the last three decades; namely, it is that over certain coefficient fields, if a homogeneous equation has a large number of variables compared to its degree, it automatically admits a non-zero solution.

Our aim is to give a complete treatment of the elementary part of the theory. This should be accessible to any undergraduate or beginning graduate student who has had a course in "modern" algebra, and the book has been written at that level. Thus, for example, the basic facts about discrete valuation rings are reviewed in Chapter 4.

We also include discussions, without complete proofs, of the more advanced results in the theory, giving appropriate references. The relations with other subjects (such as Class Field Theory, Algebraic Geometry and Analytic Number Theory) are indicated whenever possible, so that the reader will see that this theory is just one branch of a many-limbed tree. There are many problems for further research sprinkled throughout the text.

Chapter 1 is a broad survey of the entire subject,

along historical lines. Chapter 2 presents the Chevalley-Warning theorem for finite fields. Chapter 3 treats the theorems of Lang and Nagata for function fields. The next three chapters are devoted to complete discrete valuation rings, where the results are due to Lang. Chapter 7 gives complete proofs of the theorems for quadratic and cubic forms over p-adic fields; it also includes the recent counter-example of Terjanian and Schanuel, and the global theorem of Davenport is mentioned. Chapter 8 presents the theorem of Brauer and Birch, while Chapter 9 concludes with a discussion of the recent work of Ax-Kochen and Paul Cohen, in which methods of mathematical logic are introduced.

This book is an expanded version of some lectures I gave at the University of California, Santa Cruz, during the spring of 1968. I wish to thank Nicholas Burgoyne, Frank Oldham, and Eileen Wu for giving me the opportunity to try out this material. I also here express my appreciation to Marilyn Hoppman and Irmgard Wilksen for their fine job of typing the manuscript.

The symbols in brackets refer to the bibliography at the end of the book.

CONTENTS

CHAPTER 1

INTRODUCTORY SURVEY AND BASIC DEFINITIONS

Over the field of real numbers, there are many homogeneous equations such as

$$x_1^2 + x_2^2 + \cdots + x_n^2 = 0$$

which have only the trivial solution $(0,0,\ldots,0)$; here n can be any positive integer. However, there exist other fields for which the following remarkable type of statement holds: If f is a form (homogeneous polynomial) in n variables, and n is sufficiently large compared to the degree of f, then f has a non-trivial zero. The purpose of these lectures is to examine the many different fields for which such statements are known or conjectured.

The first such theorem was proved by Tsen [Ts] in

1933, almost accidentally, one might add. Tsen proved that if K is a function field in one variable over an algebraically closed field of constants, then there are no central division algebras over K (except, of course, K itself). An analysis of his proof showed that Tsen actually proved the following stronger result: If f is a form with coefficients in K of degree d in n variables, and $n > d$, then f has a non-trivial zero in K. We will show how this result implies the theorem on division algebras.

First, recall some basic facts on division algebras (see [Bb3] for the proofs). A finite-dimensional algebra D (over a field K) in which every non-zero element has an inverse and whose center is K itself is called a <u>central division algebra</u> over K. If L is an extension field of K, we can extend scalars from K to L to obtain an algebra $D_L = L \otimes_K D$ over L of the same dimension over L as D over K. A fundamental theorem states that there is a finite Galois extension L of K such that D_L is isomorphic over L to the algebra $M_n(L)$ of all n x n matrices with coefficients in L. In particular, this implies that the dimension of D over K is a square, n^2. Fixing a linear basis for D over K, we see that a typical element $x \in D$ is determined by n^2 coordinates in K. Since D is naturally embedded in D_L, choosing an isomorphism of D_L with $M_n(L)$ enables us to consider x as an n x n matrix over L. We can then take the determinant of this matrix. As a function of the coordinates of x, this determinant will be a form in n^2 variables of degree n called _the reduced norm_ $N_{red}(x)$ of x. Since x is invariant under the operations of the Galois group of L/K on D_L, the coefficients of this form will actually lie in K. Moreover, the multiplicativity of determinants implies

$$N_{red}(x)\, N_{red}(y) = N_{red}(xy)$$

for all x, y $\in$ D. Since the determinant of the identity matrix is 1, this implies

$$N_{red}(x)\, N_{red}(x^{-1}) = 1$$

for x $\neq$ 0 in D. Hence the only zero of this form in K is the trivial one. By our hypothesis, this can only happen if n = 1, i.e., D = K.

Let us restate Tsen's results in different terminology.

(1.1) DEFINITION. _Let_ K _be a field_. _Suppose that for any form_ f _with coefficients in_ K _of degree_ d _in_ n _variables_, _with_ $n > d$, f _has a non-trivial zero in_ K. _Then the field_ K _is called_ C_1.

In this language, Tsen's theorem can be broken into two parts.

(1.2) THEOREM. *If* K *is a function field in one variable over an algebraically closed field of constants*, *then* K *is* C_1.

This theorem will be proved in greater generality in Chapter 3.

(1.3) THEOREM. *If the field* K *is* C_1, *then* K *has no central division algebras*.

We have just sketched the proof of this theorem.

It is a classical theorem of Wedderburn (proved in 1905) that there are no finite non-commutative division rings. Another way of stating this is that if K is a finite field, there are no central division algebras over K. It is also a consequence of class field theory [We] that if K is the field obtained from the field of rational numbers by adjoining all roots of unity, (cyclotomic field), then there are no central division algebras over K. Comparing these results with Tsen's argument, E. Artin was led to conjecture that these fields are C_1. This was proved for finite fields in 1936 by Chevalley [C] - see Chapter 2. The conjecture for the rational cyclotomic field remains open. There is positive evidence for it in that the analogous conjecture for p-adic cyclotomic fields was proved by Lang in 1952 [Lg2] - see Chapter 6.

On the negative side, it is now known that the converse of Tsen's theorem (1.3) is false, as was pointed out by M. Auslander in the following example:

Let K_0 be the maximal solvable extension of the field of rational numbers. Let $K = K_0((t))$ be the field of formal meromorphic series over K_0. Local class field theory [S] tells us that there are no central division algebras over K. However, there exist finite extensions of K which have central division algebras. We will see in Chapter 3 that a finite extension of a C_1 field is also C_1. Hence K cannot be C_1.

A natural question suggested by this example is the following: Suppose that for every finite extension L of K, including K itself, there are no central division algebras over L. Is K then C_1? The answer to this question is also negative, as was shown by Ax [A1]. The proof involves the notions of Brauer group and cohomological dimension of a field, for which see Serre [S].

Over an algebraic number field, in particular, over the field of rational numbers, there are interesting theorems on forms in many variables for certain degrees. The oldest apparently dates back to 1883, a theorem of Meyer, which states that an indefinite quadratic form in five or more variables has a non-trivial zero [BS]. More recently, Davenport has shown, using analytic methods, that a cubic form in sixteen or more variables has a non-trivial zero [Da2]; it is conjectured that the number sixteen can be reduced to ten. More generally, Birch and Peck [B2] have shown that a form of _odd_ degree in sufficiently many variables has a non-trivial zero (see Chapter 8).

There are other fields which have nice properties with respect to forms in many variables, only more variables are needed. We therefore generalize the previous definition as follows.

(1.4) DEFINITION. _Let_ K _be a field_, $i \geq 0$ _an integer_. _Suppose that for any form_ f _with coefficients in_ K _of degree_ d _in_ n _variables, with_ $n > d^i$, f _has a non-trivial zero in_ K. _Then the field_ K _is called_ C_i.

Thus C_0 is just another symbol meaning "algebraically closed".

We will see in Chapter 3 that if K is a function field in j variables over a field of constants which is C_i, then K is C_{i+j} (generalizing Tsen's theorem 1.2). It is also the case that a field of formal meromorphic series in one variable over a field which is C_i is C_{i+1} [Gb]. Artin conjectured that p-adic fields are C_2. Recent counterexamples showed that this conjecture is false, but work of Ax and Kochen shows that Artin's conjecture is "almost true" - see Chapter 7 for the precise statement.

Thus the technique of Tsen's proof has led to a fascinating new area of research.

Note: The terminology "C_i" was introduced in Lang's thesis [Lg2], which was the first systematic treatment of these results. C_1 fields have also been called "quasi algebraically closed".

CHAPTER 2

FINITE FIELDS

Let k be a finite field with q elements. Let the prime number p be the characteristic of k. Then the elements $0, 1, \ldots, (p - 1)\cdot 1$ of k form the smallest subfield of k (the prime subfield), and this subfield is canonically isomorphic to the field $\underline{\underline{Z}}/p$ of integers mod p. If ν is the dimension of k as a vector space over $\underline{\underline{Z}}/p$, then $q = p^{\nu}$.

Let k^* be the multiplicative group of non-zero elements of k, so that k^* has $q - 1$ elements. We need to know that k^* is actually <u>cyclic</u> of order $q - 1$. This can be seen as follows: If k^* were not cyclic, the elementary theory of finite abelian groups tells us that the least common multiple m of all the orders of the elements of k^* has to be a proper divisor of $q - 1$. But then the equation $x^m = 1$ would have more than m distinct roots in the field k, which is impossible.

As an application of this result, we will prove the following lemma.

(2.1) LEMMA. Given an integer $m > 0$, we have

$$\sum_{x \in k} x^m = \begin{cases} -1 & \text{if } q - 1 \text{ divides } m \\ 0 & \text{otherwise} \end{cases}$$

Proof. The function $x \to x^m$ is a homomorphism of the group k^* into itself. Since k^* is cyclic of order $q - 1$, this homomorphism is trivial only when m is divisible by $q - 1$, and in that case the sum is $(q - 1) \cdot 1 \equiv -1$. If m is not divisible by $q - 1$, the result follows from the following more general lemma.

(2.2) LEMMA. Let Ω be any field, and let $h: k^* \to \Omega^*$ be any non-trivial homomorphism of the multiplicative group of k into that of Ω. Then

$$\sum_{x \in k^*} h(x) = 0$$

Proof. By hypothesis $h(y) \neq 1$ for some $y \in k^*$. Then

$$\sum_{x \in k^*} h(x) = \sum_{x \in k^*} h(yx) = h(y) \sum_{x \in k^*} h(x)$$

since h is a homomorphism, and the lemma is proved. ⌟

Our aim is to prove that k is C_1, i.e., that every homogeneous polynomial in more variables than its degree has a non-trivial zero in k. Without any extra work, we can actually prove a stronger result.

(2.3) THEOREM (CHEVALLEY-WARNING). *Let* f *be a polynomial in* n *variables with coefficients in the finite field* k, *and let* d *be its degree. Let* N(f) *be the number of distinct zeros of* f *in* k. *If* $n > d$ *then*

$$N(f) \equiv 0 \pmod{p}$$

In particular, if f *has no constant term, then* f *has a non-trivial zero in* k.

Proof (Ax [A2]). For each n-tuple $x \in K^n$, we have

$$1 - f(x)^{q-1} = \begin{cases} 1 & \text{if } f(x) = 0 \\ 0 & \text{otherwise} \end{cases}$$

Summing over all $x \in K^n$, we get

$$\overline{N(f)} = \sum (1 - f(x)^{q-1}) = -\sum f(x)^{q-1}$$

where $\overline{N(f)}$ is the residue class mod p of N(f), considered as an element of k. Thus we must prove that for any polynomial f with $d < n$, we have

$$\sum_{x \in k^n} f(x)^{q-1} = 0$$

Now f^{q-1}, being of degree $d(q-1)$, is a k-linear combination of monomials of degree at most $d(q-1)$. If $X^{\mu} = X_1^{\mu_1} X_2^{\mu_2} \cdots X_n^{\mu_n}$ is one such monomial, we compute

$$\sum_{x \in k^n} x^{\mu} = \prod_{i=1}^{n} \sum_{x_i \in k} x_i^{\mu_i}$$

Since $d < n$, at least one μ_i is not divisible by $q - 1$, and by Lemma 2.1, the $i^{\underline{th}}$ term in the above product will then be zero.

Note. One can say more about the number of zeros N(f). Ax [A2] has shown that in fact N(f) is divisible by q, not merely by p; the proof uses Gauss sums. The precise statement is that if b is the largest integer strictly less than n/d, then q^b divides N(f). Ax also gives an example of a polynomial f such that the highest power of p dividing N(f) is exactly q^b, so his divisibility result is best possible. On the other hand, Warning [Wa] showed that if $d < n$ and f has at least one zero in k then $N(f) \geq q^{n-d}$; the proof uses only elementary linear algebra. General theorems estimating the number of solutions of equations in finite fields will be found in the paper of Lang and Weil [LW]; the proofs in this paper are based on some deep results in algebraic geometry. These questions are closely related to the theory of zeta functions of algebraic varieties over finite fields [Lu].

CHAPTER 3

FUNCTION FIELDS

We say that a field K is _a function field in_ j _variables over a field of constants_ k if one of the following equivalent conditions is satisfied:

(i) K is a finite extension of a field of rational functions in j independent variables over k.

(ii) K has transcendence degree j over k and is finitely generated over k, i.e., K is obtained from k by adjoining finitely many elements.

We will generalize Tsen's theorem and show that if k is C_i then K is C_{i+j}. We will see, in fact, that the assumption "K finitely generated over k" is unnecessary. First some preliminaries.

Let ϕ be a form of degree d in n variables with coefficients in a field K. If the only zero of ϕ in K is the trivial one, and if $n = d^i$, then ϕ is called <u>normic of order</u> i; when $i = 1$, we say simply ϕ is <u>normic</u>. The next lemma explains the origin of this terminology.

(3.1) LEMMA. *Suppose K has a finite extension E of degree $e > 1$. Then the norm from E to K is a normic form of degree e.*

Proof. The norm $N(x)$ of $x \in E$ is defined to be the determinant of the linear transformation "multiplication by x". Once a basis for E as a vector space over K has been chosen, $N(x)$ becomes a homogeneous polynomial of degree e in the e coordinates of x. Since $N(x) \neq 0$ for $x \neq 0$, this form is normic.

∎

This lemma shows that the inequality $n > d$ in Chevalley's theorem (2.3) cannot be improved. For given any d, a finite field has an extension of degree d, hence a normic form of degree d.

For technical purposes later on, we will need another lemma.

(3.2) LEMMA. *If K is not algebraically closed, then K admits normic forms of arbitrarily large degree.*

This lemma is not an immediate corollary of the previous one, because K need not admit extensions of arbitrarily large degree. For instance, if K is the field of real numbers, it only has an extension of degree 2. Nevertheless, the lemma is obviously true for the reals. Moreover, a theorem of Artin-Schreier states that fields like the reals are the only ones whose algebraic closure is a finite extension.

Here is a simple proof which avoids the use of Artin-Schreier: Let ϕ be normic of degree e. Let

$$\phi^{(1)} = \phi(\phi|\phi| \cdots |\phi)$$

$$\phi^{(2)} = \phi^{(1)}(\phi|\phi| \cdots |\phi)$$

etc., where we substitute the form ϕ itself for each variable, and the slashes mean each new occurrence of ϕ has new variables. Then $\phi^{(m)}$ is clearly normic of degree e^m. ⌟

We need one more preliminary result about systems of homogeneous equations. First we recall a classical theorem.

(3.3) THEOREM. _Suppose_ K _is algebraically closed_. _If_ $f_1,\ldots,f_r$ _are forms in_ n _variables over_ K _and_ $n > r$, _then these forms have a common non-trivial zero in_ K.

This theorem can be proved by brute force using elimination theory, but there is a nice geometric way to see it. The set of zeros of the form f_j in projective (n - 1)-space over K forms a _hypersurface_ H_j, i.e., a projective variety of dimension $n - 2$. The above theorem states that the intersection $H_1 \cap H_2 \cap \cdots \cap H_r$ of these hypersurfaces is non-empty. In fact, the theory of dimension in projective spaces states that this intersection has dimension $\geq n - r - 1$ [Lg1]. ⌟

We can now state the generalization of this to C_i fields. (If x is a real number, the symbol $[x]$ will always mean the largest integer less than or equal to x.)

(3.4) THEOREM (LANG-NAGATA). _Let_ K _be a_ C_i _field. Let_ $f_1, \ldots, f_r$ _be forms in_ n _variables of degree_ d. _If_ $n > rd^i$ _they have a non-trivial common zero in_ K.

Proof. We can assume K is not algebraically closed, otherwise the theorem is classical (3.3). Let ϕ be a normic form of degree $e \geq r$. Consider the sequence of forms

$$\phi^{(1)} = \phi^{(1)}(f) = \phi(f_1,\ldots,f_r|f_1,\ldots,f_r|\ldots|f_1,\ldots,f_r|0,\ldots,0)$$

$$\phi^{(2)} = \phi^{(2)}(f) = \phi^{(1)}(f_1,\ldots,f_r|f_1,\ldots,f_r|\ldots|f_1,\ldots,f_r|0,\ldots,0)$$

etc. where after each slash we use new variables, and we insert as many complete sets of f's as possible.

Thus $\phi^{(1)}$ has $n[\frac{e}{r}]$ variables and has degree $de \leq dr([\frac{e}{r}] + 1)$. If K is C_1, we want

$$n[\frac{e}{r}] > dr([\frac{e}{r}] + 1)$$

or

$$(n - dr)[\frac{e}{r}] > dr$$

Since $n - dr > 0$, this can be arranged by taking e large. Then $\phi^{(1)}$ has a non-trivial zero, which, since ϕ is normic, is a common zero of all the f's.

If K is C_i with $i > 1$, we have to use the higher $\phi^{(m)}$'s. Now $\phi^{(m)}$ has degree $D_m = d^m e$, and if N_m is the number of variables in $\phi^{(m)}$,

$$N_{m+1} = [\frac{N_m}{r}]$$

We want to choose m so large that $N_m > (D_m)^i$. Now $[\frac{N_m}{r}] = \frac{N_m}{r} - \frac{t_m}{r}$, where $0 \leq t_m < r$. Hence

$$\begin{aligned} \frac{N_{m+1}}{(D_{m+1})^i} &= \frac{n[\frac{N_m}{r}]}{d^i (D_m)^i} \\ &= \frac{n}{rd^i}\frac{N_m}{(D_m)^i} - \frac{n}{rd^i}\frac{t_m}{e^i (d^i)^m} \\ &\geq \frac{n}{rd^i}\frac{N_m}{(D_m)^i} - \frac{n}{rd^i}\frac{r}{e^i (d^i)^m} \end{aligned}$$

Using the same inequality for m, m - 1, ... 2, we get

$$\frac{N_{m+1}}{(D_{m+1})^i} \ge \left(\frac{n}{rd^i}\right)^2\left(\frac{N_{m-1}}{(D_{m-1})^i} - \frac{r}{e^i(d^i)^{m-1}}\right) - \left(\frac{n}{rd^i}\right)\left(\frac{r}{e^i(d^i)^m}\right)$$

$$\vdots$$

$$\ge \left(\frac{n}{rd^i}\right)^m \frac{N_1}{(D_1)^i} - \frac{r}{e^i}\,\frac{n}{r}\,\frac{1}{(d^i)^{m+1}}\left(\left(\frac{n}{r}\right)^{m-1} + \left(\frac{n}{r}\right)^{m-2} \cdots + 1\right)$$

$$= \left(\frac{n}{rd^i}\right)^m \frac{N_1}{(D_1)^i} - \frac{r}{e^i}\,\frac{n}{r}\,\frac{1}{(d^i)^{m+1}}\,\frac{(\frac{n}{r})^m - 1}{(\frac{n}{r}) - 1}$$

Substituting $D_1 = de$, $N_1 = n[\frac{e}{r}]$, $[\frac{e}{r}] = \frac{e}{r} - \frac{t}{r}$, $0 \le t < r$, we get (using some algebra on the second term)

$$\frac{N_{m+1}}{(D_{m+1})^i} \ge \left(\frac{n}{rd^i}\right)^{m+1} \frac{e-t}{e^i} - \frac{r}{e^i}\,\frac{n}{r}\,\frac{1}{(d^i)^{m+1}}\,\frac{r(n^m - r^m)}{r^m(n-r)}$$

$$= \left(\frac{n}{rd^i}\right)^{m+1} \frac{e-t}{e^i} - \frac{r}{e^i}\,\frac{n}{rd^i}\,\frac{r}{n-r}\left(\left(\frac{n}{rd^i}\right)^m - \frac{1}{(d^i)^m}\right)$$

$$= \left(\frac{n}{rd^i}\right)^{m+1}\left(\frac{e-t}{e^i} - \frac{r^2}{e^i(n-r)}\right) + \frac{1}{(d^i)^m}\left(\frac{rn}{e^i d^i(n-r)}\right)$$

$$= \left(\frac{n}{rd^i}\right)^{m+1}\left(\frac{(n-r)(e-t) - r^2}{e^i(n-r)}\right) + \frac{1}{(d^i)^m}\left(\frac{rn}{e^i d^i(n-r)}\right)$$

Since e can be chosen so large that $(n-r)(e-t) - r^2 > 0$, and $\left(\frac{n}{rd^i}\right) > 1$, the first term goes to ∞ as $m \to \infty$. The second term goes to zero ($d > 1$). Therefore, $\frac{N_m}{(D_m)^i} \to \infty$ as $m \to \infty$, and we are done.

Note. Lang [Lg2] generalized this theorem to the case where the f's have different degrees $d_1,\ldots,d_r$ and $n > d_1^i + \cdots + d_r^i$, but only under the extra hypothesis that K has a normic form of order i of every degree. It would be interesting to remove this hypothesis if possible.

(3.5) THEOREM. *If the field K is C_i so is every algebraic extension of K.*

Proof (Lang). It suffices to prove the theorem for a finite extension E of K, since the coefficients of any given form lie in a finite extension.

Let $f(X_1,\ldots,X_n)$ be a form in E with $n > d^i$. Let $\omega_1,\ldots,\omega_e$ be a basis for E as vector space over K. Introduce new variables $\overline{X}_{\nu\mu}$ with

$$X_\nu = \overline{X}_{\nu 1}\omega_1 + \overline{X}_{\nu 2}\omega_2 + \cdots + \overline{X}_{\nu e}\omega_e$$

$\nu = 1,\ldots,n$. Then $f(X) = f_1(\overline{X})\omega_1 + \cdots + f_e(\overline{X})\omega_e$, where $f_1,\ldots,f_e$ are forms of degree d in en variables and coefficients in K. Finding a zero of f in E is equivalent to finding a common zero of $f_1,\ldots,f_e$ in K. But this can be done by the previous theorem, since $en > ed^i$.

┘

(3.6) THEOREM. *If the field* K *is* C_i *and* E *is an extension of* K *of transcendence degree* j, *then* E *is* C_{i+j}.

Proof (Tsen, essentially). E is an algebraic extension of a purely transcendental extension of K. By the previous theorem and induction on j , we are reduced to the case $E = K(T)$. By homogeneity, it suffices to consider forms with coefficients in the polynomial ring K[T].

Suppose $f(X_1,\dots,X_n)$ has $n > d^{i+1}$ and coefficients in K[T]. Introduce new variables $\overline{X}_{\nu\mu}$ with

$$X_\nu = \overline{X}_{\nu 0} + \overline{X}_{\nu 1}T + \overline{X}_{\nu 2}T^2 + \dots + \overline{X}_{\nu s}T^s$$

$\nu = 1,\dots,n$, where s will be specified later. If r is the highest degree of the coefficients of f, we get

$$f(X) = f_0(\overline{X}) + f_1(\overline{X})T + \dots + f_{ds+r}(\overline{X})T^{ds+r}$$

where each f_μ is a form of degree d in $n(s + 1)$ variables. We can apply theorem (3.4) to these forms with coefficients in K provided that

$$n(s + 1) > d^i(ds + r + 1)$$

or

$$(n - d^{i+1})\, s > d^i(r + 1) - n$$

This can be satisfied by taking s large. The common non-trivial zero of the f_μ's in K gives a non-trivial zero of f in K[T]. ⌟

CHAPTER 4

COMPLETE DISCRETE VALUATION RINGS

Let k be any field. Consider the ring $R = k[[T]]$ whose elements are all formal power series

$$x = x_0 + x_1 T + x_2 T^2 + \cdots + x_n T^n + \cdots$$

in the variable T with coefficients $x_j \in k$. We define a function v on the non-zero elements of this ring by

$$v(x) = n$$

provided $x_0 = \cdots = x_{n-1} = 0$, and $x_n \neq 0$. Obviously the function v has the following properties:

(i) $v(xy) = v(x) + v(y)$

(ii) if $v(x) \neq v(y)$, then $v(x + y) = \min\{v(x), v(y)\}$, whereas if $v(x) = v(y)$, then $v(x + y) \geq \min\{v(x), v(y)\}$.

Somewhat less obvious is the next property.

(iii) $v(x) = 0$ if and only if x is a unit in R, i.e., x has an inverse x^{-1} in R.

Proof. It is clear from (i) or from the definition that $v(1) = 0$ so that $v(x) = 0$ if x^{-1} is also in R. Conversely, if $v(x) = 0$, i.e., the constant term x_0 is non-zero, we can write

$$x = x_0(1 + y)$$

where y is a power series without constant term. Then the geometric series

$$\frac{1}{1 + y} = 1 - y + y^2 + \dots + (-1)^n y^n + \dots$$

is again a power series in T, so that $x^{-1} = x_0^{-1}(1 + y)^{-1}$ is in R. ┘

In general, suppose we have a pair (R, v) consisting of an integral domain R and a function v mapping R onto the set of non-negative integers so as to satisfy conditions (i), (ii) and (iii). We say R is a discrete valuation ring with valuation v. The proofs of the following statements are left as easy exercises for the reader (we define $v(0) = \infty$).

(iv) Given an integer $n > 0$, the set I_n of all $x \in R$ such that $v(x) \geq n$ is a proper ideal in R.

(v) $I = I_1$ is a prime ideal, in fact, a maximal ideal.

(vi) Let K be the field of fractions of R. If we allow v to take on negative values, then there is a unique extension of v to K which still satisfies properties (i) and (ii). (Specifically, if a non-zero element of K is represented as a fraction x/y, then $v(x/y) = v(x) - v(y)$.) Once this extension has been made, the set of all $z \in K$ such that $v(z) \geq 0$ is just the domain R.

(vii) Let $\pi \in R$ be any element such that $v(\pi) = 1$ (called a uniformizing parameter). Then for any $n > 0$, π^n generates the ideal I_n. Since these are the only proper ideals in R, R is a principal ideal domain.

(viii) If x is a non-zero element of K, then x can be expressed uniquely in the form

$$x = u\pi^n$$

where $n = v(x)$ and u is a unit in R.

(ix) Consider the ring $R_n = R/\pi^{n+1}$ of cosets modulo π^{n+1}. Denote by k the residue field R_0. Choose arbitrarily a system of representatives of k in R, i.e., a one-to-one mapping $\alpha \to \{\alpha\}$ of k into R. Given $a \in R$, if α_0 is the coset of a mod π, then $a - \{\alpha_0\}$ is divisible by π, say $a - \{\alpha_0\} = a_1\pi$, $a_1 \in R$. If α_1 is the coset of a_1 mod π, then $a_1 - \{\alpha_1\} = a_2\pi$, $a_2 \in R$, so that

$$a \equiv \{\alpha_0\} + \{\alpha_1\}\,\pi \pmod{\pi^2}$$

Continuing in this way, we see that for any $n > 0$, the elements of R_n are represented uniquely by all the elements of R of the form

$$\{\alpha_0\} + \{\alpha_1\} \pi + \cdots + \{\alpha_n\} \pi^n$$

$\alpha_0, \ldots, \alpha_n \in k$. Under this representation, the canonical ring homomorphism $\phi_n \colon R_n \to R_{n-1}$ (which sends the coset of an element mod π^{n+1} into the coset of that same element mod π^n) can be described by omitting the last term $\{\alpha_n\} \pi^n$ in the above expansion.

(4.1) EXAMPLE. In case $R = k[[T]]$, we can take $\pi = T$ as uniformizing parameter, and as representatives of k the elements of k themselves. Property (viii) shows that the elements of the field of fractions K are those formal Laurent series

$$\sum_{-\infty}^{\infty} x_n T^n$$

such that at most finitely many of the x_n with n negative are different from zero (formal meromorphic series).

Returning to the general case, consider the system of rings and homomorphisms

$$k = R_0 \overset{\phi_1}{\leftarrow} R_1 \overset{\phi_2}{\leftarrow} \cdots \overset{\phi_n}{\leftarrow} R_n \leftarrow \cdots$$

The direct product of all these rings consists of all infinite sequences $(\xi_0, \xi_1, \ldots, \xi_n, \ldots)$, where $\xi_n \in R_n$ for all n; this set forms a ring when we add and multiply two sequences component by component. Consider the subset $\hat{R}$ of the direct product consisting of the <u>compatible sequences</u>, i.e., sequences such that

$$\phi_n \xi_n = \xi_{n-1}$$

for all $n > 0$. Clearly $\hat{R}$ is a subring of the direct product; it is called the <u>completion</u> of R.

There is a canonical homomorphism

$$\iota : R \to \hat{R}$$

which assigns to any $x \in R$ the sequence whose n^{th} component is the coset of x mod π^{n+1}. The homomorphism ι is an embedding of R into $\hat{R}$, since the only element of R divisible by all positive powers of π is the zero element. By means of the embedding ι, we will regard R as a subring of $\hat{R}$. If it then turns out that $R = \hat{R}$, we say that R is <u>complete</u>.

The completion $\hat{R}$ may seem like a formidable object, but it actually has a very simple description. Namely, it follows from (ix) that the elements of $\hat{R}$ are in one-to-one correspondence with the "infinite series" of the form

(4.2) $$\{\alpha_0\} + \{\alpha_1\}\pi + \cdots + \{\alpha_n\}\pi^n + \cdots$$

Using this representation, the valuation v can be extended to $\hat{R}$ by defining the valuation of such a series to be the first n such that $\alpha_n \neq 0$. Clearly the valuation of an element of R computed this way is the same as it was before. Moreover, it is an easy exercise to show that $\hat{R}$ is an integral domain which is a valuation ring for the extended valuation v. Also, the residue rings of $\hat{R}$ are the same as those of R

$$\hat{R}/\pi^{n+1} = R/\pi^{n+1}$$

so that $\hat{R}$ is indeed complete.

Note. We will see in Chapter 5 that the "infinite series" (4.2), which at the moment is just a shorthand notation for the compatible sequence

$$(\alpha_0, \ldots, \text{coset of } \{\alpha_0\} + \cdots + \{\alpha_n\}\pi^n \bmod \pi^{n+1}, \ldots)$$

can actually be interpreted as a converging infinite series with respect to an appropriate metric on R, and that the algebraic notion of completeness defined above coincides with the convergence notion of completeness in a metric space. ⌟

Since every element of k[[T]] is already an infinite series, it is clear that k[[T]] is complete. In fact, the representation (4.2) may suggest that, up to isomorphism, the only complete discrete valuation ring with residue field k is the ring k[[T]]. That is in fact true (see 5.18) when k has characteristic 0, but not otherwise! The point is that although the series (4.2) look like power series, they do not necessarily add and multiply in the simple way that power series do, as the next example shows.

(4.3) EXAMPLE. Let p be a prime number. Define a valuation v on the ring $\mathbb{Z}$ of integers by $v(a) = n$ if p^n is the highest power of p dividing a. If $v(a) = n$, $v(b) = m$, then clearly p^{n+m} is the highest power of p dividing ab, so property (i) holds. If $n < m$, then surely p^n is the highest power of p dividing $a + b$, whereas if $n = m$, p^n and possibly a higher power of p divides $a + b$; thus (ii) holds.

Property (iii), however, does not hold, so we must pass from the ring $\mathbb{Z}$ to a larger ring if we want to obtain a valuation ring. Namely, we want integers b such that $v(b) = 0$ (i.e., integers b which are not divisible by p) to become units. We therefore take R to consist of all rational numbers of the form a/b, where $p \nmid b$, and define the valuation of such a number to be the valuation of its numerator. Clearly R is a valuation ring. This valuation ring has a canonical uniformizing parameter, namely the prime p.

Moreover, it is a nice exercise in quotient rings to

see that

$$R_n = \underline{\underline{Z}}/p^{n+1}$$

the ring of integers mod p^{n+1}. As representatives of

$$k = \underline{\underline{Z}}/p$$

we can therefore take the integers $0,1,\ldots, p - 1$. Thus the elements of the completion are represented by infinite series

$$a_0 + a_1p + a_2p^2 + \cdots + a_np^n + \cdots$$

where $0 \leq a_n < p$ for all n. This completion will be denoted $\underline{\underline{Z}}_p$ and called the ring of p-<u>adic integers</u>. It was discovered by K. Hensel early in this century. Since $\underline{\underline{Z}} \subset \underline{\underline{Z}}_p$, $\underline{\underline{Z}}_p$ has characteristic zero, whereas its residue field $\underline{\underline{Z}}/p$ has characteristic p. Hence $\underline{\underline{Z}}_p$ is not isomorphic to $(\underline{\underline{Z}}/p)[[T]]$. In fact, if you take two ordinary positive integers and express them by their (finite) p-adic expansions, it is clear that the expansions do not add and multiply like formal power series.

<u>Note</u>. The p-adic expansion of a negative integer need not be finite. For example, in $\underline{\underline{Z}}_2$, we have the remarkable formula

$$-1 = \frac{1}{1 - 2} = 1 + 2 + 4 + 8 + \cdots + 2^n + \cdots$$

which can be checked by adding 1 to both sides.

The field of fractions $\underline{\underline{Q}}_p$ of $\underline{\underline{Z}}_p$ is called the field of p-adic numbers. ⌟

Let R be any complete discrete valuation ring, k its residue field, π a uniformizing parameter. Let us consider the problem of solving algebraic equations over R.

Given a system $f_1,\ldots,f_r$ of polynomials in n variables with coefficients in R. We wish to find a vector $x = (x_1,\ldots,x_n) \in R^n$ such that

$$(4.4) \qquad f_j(x) = 0 \qquad j = 1,\ldots,r$$

Clearly a necessary condition for the existence of a common zero is that the congruences

$$(4.5) \qquad f_j(x) \equiv 0 \pmod{\pi^{m+1}} \qquad j = 1,\ldots,r$$

have a solution for all $m = 0,1,\ldots$; since R is complete, the converse turns out to be true as well.

(4.6) THEOREM. *The equations* (4.4) *have a common zero in* R *if and only if for each* $m \geq 0$, *the congruences* (4.5) *have a common solution in* R.

We will prove this theorem and the next one only under the following compactness assumption: *Assume the residue rings* $R_m = R/\pi^{m+1}$ *are finite for all* m. This assumption is satisfied, for example, by $\underline{\underline{Z}}_p$ and by a power series ring with coefficients in a finite field. The theorems can be proved without this assumption, using a little algebraic geometry and Hensel's Lemma -- see [Gb] and (5.24).

Proof. We will consider n-tuples with coordinates in R_m. If ϕ_m: $R_m \to R_{m-1}$ is the canonical homomorphism, applying ϕ_m to each coordinate gives a mapping $(R_m)^n \to (R_{m-1})^n$ also denoted ϕ_m.

For each m, let $S_m \subset (R_m)^n$ be the set of solutions of the given equations in the ring R_m. By hypothesis, S_m is non-empty for all m.

Fix m for the moment. For every $j > m$, let $S_{j,m}$ be the image of S_j under the composite mapping $\phi_{m+1} \cdots \phi_{j-1}\phi_j$. We then have a decreasing sequence of non-empty sets

$$S_m \supset S_{m+1,m} \supset \cdots \supset S_{j,m} \supset \cdots$$

Since these sets are finite, their intersection T_m must also be non-empty. T_m consists of those solutions mod π^{m+1} which lift to solutions mod π^{j+1} for all $j > m$.

Clearly $\phi_m(T_m) \subset T_{m-1}$, and in fact we claim these sets are equal: If $\xi_{m-1} \in T_{m-1}$, then by definition of T_{m-1}, the fibre $\phi_m^{-1}(\xi_{m-1})$ meets $S_{j,m}$ for all $j \geq m$, hence it meets T_m.

Thus we can start with a solution $\xi_0 \in T_0$, pick a solution $\xi_1 \in T_1$ such that $\phi_1\xi_1 = \xi_0$, etc. We obtain by induction a compatible sequence of solutions $(\xi_0, \xi_1, \ldots)$, which -- since R is complete -- is a solution in R.

$\lrcorner$

Suppose now the polynomials $f_1,\ldots,f_r$ are homogeneous. In that case we will want a common _non-trivial_ zero in R, so the above argument must be modified. If we had such a zero x, then dividing all the coordinates of x by an appropriate power of π, we can (by homogeneity) insure that some coordinate is a unit -- in that case we say that x is a _primitive_ solution.

(4.7) THEOREM. _The homogeneous equations_ (4.4) _have a primitive solution in_ R _if and only if for each_ $m \geq 0$, _the congruences_ (4.5) _have a primitive solution in_ R.

The exact same proof works, provided we restrict ourselves to primitive vectors (clearly ϕ_m maps a primitive vector in $(R_m)^n$ into a primitive vector in $(R_{m-1})^n$).

┘

Here is an important application.

(4.8) THEOREM. _Let_ k _be a_ C_i _field, and let_ k((T)) _be the field of formal meromorphic series in one variable_ T _over_ k. _Then_ k((T)) _is_ C_{i+1}.

Proof. Let f be a form in n variables of degree d with coefficients in k((T)), and suppose $n > d^{i+1}$. Multiplying by a common denominator, we can assume the coefficients of f are power series, and we then want a primitive zero of f in $k[[T]]$. By (4.7), it suffices to find a primitive zero in the residue ring mod T^{m+1} for each m. To accomplish that, we can ignore those terms in the coefficients of f involving powers of T greater than the $m^{\underline{th}}$ power, so that the coefficients are polynomials in T. But then (3.6) tells us that the polynomial ring $k[T]$ is C_{i+1}, so we are done. ⌟

(4.9) COROLLARY. <u>If</u> k <u>is a finite field then</u> $k((T))$ <u>is</u> C_2.

This follows from the theorem of Chevalley (2.3). ⌟

Taking $k = \mathbb{Z}/p$, one might consider this corollary as evidence for the conjecture that $\mathbb{Q}_p$ is C_2. We will see in Chapter 9 that there is an important relation between the fields $\mathbb{Q}_p$ and $\mathbb{Z}/p((T))$, even though $\mathbb{Q}_p$ is not C_2.

<u>Note</u>. If one considers the field of formal meromorphic series in several variables $k((T_1,\ldots,T_j))$ over a C_i field k, it is not known whether this field is C_{i+j} when $j \geq 2$. A simple induction does not work because, e.g., $k((T_1, T_2))$ is not the same as $k((T_1))((T_2))$!

<u>Note</u>. The result (4.8) is best possible, for we have the following proposition (Lang).

(4.10) PROPOSITION. <u>Let</u> R <u>be a discrete valuation ring with residue field</u> k. <u>If there is a form</u> ϕ <u>over</u> k <u>of degree</u> d *which is normic of order* $i \geq 0$, *then there is a form* Φ *of degree* d *over* R *which is normic of order* $i + 1$.

Proof. By hypothesis, ϕ has $n = d^i$ variables and has only the trivial zero in k. Let π be a uniformizing parameter in R. Let ϕ' be a form of degree d over R obtained from ϕ by replacing each coefficient of ϕ by a representative in R. Let $V_1,\ldots,V_d$ be independent vectors of n variables each, and consider the form

$$\Phi(V_1,\ldots,V_d) = \phi'(V_1) + \pi\phi'(V_2) + \pi^2\phi'(V_3) + \cdots + \pi^{d-1}\phi'(V_d)$$

Φ has degree d in d^{i+1} variables. We claim Φ has no primitive zero mod π^d: For suppose

$$\Phi(v_1,v_2,\ldots,v_d) \equiv 0 \pmod{\pi^d} \tag{1}$$

where each $v_i \in R^n$. Reading this congruence mod π gives

$$\phi'(v_1) \equiv 0 \pmod{\pi}$$

Since ϕ is normic of order i, v_1 is not primitive, i.e., $v_1 = \pi w_1$ for some $w_1 \in R^n$. But then

$$\phi'(v_1) = \pi^d\phi'(w_1)$$

by homogeneity. Hence the congruence (1) can be divided by π to give

$$\phi'(v_2) + \pi\phi'(v_3) + \cdots + \pi^{d-2}\phi'(v_d) \equiv 0 \pmod{\pi^{d-1}}$$

Repeating the above argument we see that v_2 is not primitive, and continuing in this way, we see that none of the vectors v_i can be primitive.

$\lrcorner$

CHAPTER 5

HENSEL'S LEMMA

The criterion (4.6) for solvability of a system of equations in a complete discrete valuation ring R involves solving the analogous congruences modulo all the powers of the uniformizing parameter π. The lemma of Hensel-Rychlik, on the other hand, enables us to deduce a solution in R from the solvability of just one of those congruences, provided the latter solution is "sufficiently non-singular".

In the case of a polynomial in one variable, we will prove Hensel's Lemma by Newton's method. Then we will prove a version for several polynomials in more than one variable by the method of N. Bourbaki. The latter version includes the former as a special case, but it is instructive to have two proofs.

Let us recall how Newton's method works over the field $\mathbb{R}$ of real numbers. Given a function ϕ of a real variable, we will need to consider the iterates of ϕ defined by

$$\phi^2(x) = \phi(\phi(x))$$

$$\phi^{n+1}(x) = \phi(\phi^n(x)) \qquad n \geq 0$$

The process of iteration will enable us to find a _fixed point_ of ϕ, i.e., a real number ξ such that

$$\phi(\xi) = \xi$$

In order for the iterates to converge to a fixed point, we will need to assume that the function ϕ is a _contraction_, i.e., that ϕ is differentiable on an interval J and that there exists a number $\zeta < 1$ such that the derivative of ϕ satisfies

$$| \phi'(x) | < \zeta < 1 \qquad \text{all } x \in J$$

(5.1) LEMMA. _If_ ϕ _is a contraction on an interval_ J _and_ ϕ _has a fixed point_ ξ _in_ J, _then beginning with any point_ $x_0 \in J$, _the sequence of iterates_

$$x_n = \phi^n(x_0) \qquad n = 1, 2, \ldots$$

converges to ξ. _In particular_ (_starting with_ $x_0 = \xi$), ξ _is the unique fixed point of_ ϕ _in_ J.

Proof. By the mean value theorem,

$$\phi(x_0) - \phi(\xi) = \phi(x_0) - \xi = (x_0 - \xi)\ \phi'(\overline{x_0})$$

where $\overline{x_0}$ is between x_0 and ξ. Thus

$$| x_1 - \xi | < \zeta | x_0 - \xi |$$

so that x_1 is closer to ξ than x_0. By the same argument applied repeatedly, we see that

$$| x_n - \xi | < \zeta^n | x_0 - \xi |$$

for all $n \geq 1$, hence the sequence converges to ξ. ⌟

Let us apply this to the problem of finding a zero of a smooth function f in an interval J. We will assume that f is either increasing or decreasing throughout the interval J, i.e., that f' is differentiable and never zero in J.

We can then be sure that f has a zero in J if the sign of f at one end-point of J is different from the sign at the other end-point. To approximate the zero as close as we like, consider the function

$$\phi(x) = x - \frac{f(x)}{f'(x)}$$

and note that the zero of f is the fixed point of ϕ. We can then use the above iteration process on ϕ provided ϕ is a contraction. A computation shows

$$\phi'(x) = \frac{f(x)f''(x)}{f'(x)^2} \tag{5.2}$$

Applying the above lemma gives our result.

(5.3) NEWTON'S LEMMA. *Assume the function* f *has a zero in the interval* J *and that its derivative* f' *is differentiable and never zero in* J. *Assume further there exists* $\zeta < 1$ *such that*

$$\left|\frac{f(x)f''(x)}{f'(x)^2}\right| < \zeta \qquad \text{all } x \in J$$

Then beginning with any $x_0 \in J$, *the sequence*

$$x_{n+1} = x_n - \frac{f(x_n)}{f'(x_n)} \qquad n = 0,1,\ldots$$

converges to the unique zero of f *in* J.

Note. The conclusion of Newton's lemma actually holds under a hypothesis easier to check than the contraction hypothesis. Namely, it suffices to assume instead that the second derivative f'' doesn't vanish in J. For then the above sequence either increases and is bounded above by the zero ξ, or decreases and is bounded below by ξ. Hence the sequence converges, and since the limit of the sequence is (by continuity of ϕ) a zero of f, it must be equal to the unique zero ξ. The advantages of the contraction hypothesis are that it gives an estimate of how close x_n is to ξ, and secondly, it is the hypothesis which has an analogue for complete discrete valuation rings.

Once again, let R be a complete discrete valuation ring with valuation v, uniformizing parameter π, residue field k, and field of fractions K. Choose once and for all a real number $\gamma > 1$; a standard choice is $\gamma = e$, or when $K = \mathbb{Q}_p$, $\gamma = p$. Define an absolute value on K by

$$|x| = \gamma^{-v(x)}$$

for $x \neq 0$, and set $|0| = 0$. This function satisfies

$$(5.4) \qquad |xy| = |x|\,|y|$$

$$(5.5) \qquad |x + y| \leq \max\{|x|, |y|\}$$

as follows at once from properties (i) and (ii) in the definition of valuation in Chapter 4. Note that if $|x| \neq |y|$, equality holds in (5.5), by property (ii). Condition (5.5) implies

$$(5.6) \qquad |x + y| \leq |x| + |y|$$

so that if we define the distance between x and y to be

$|x - y|$, K becomes a metric space. Note that $x \in R$ if and only if $|x| \le 1$.

(5.7) PROPOSITION. *If* R *is a complete discrete valuation ring then* K *is a complete metric space*, *and conversely*.

Proof. Let (x_n) be a sequence of elements of K. To say that this sequence converges to a limit $x \in K$ means that given any real $\varepsilon > 0$, there exists an integer $N = N(\varepsilon)$ such that

$$|x - x_n| < \varepsilon$$

for all $n \ge N$. In terms of the valuation, this becomes

$$v(x - x_n) > - \log_\gamma \varepsilon$$

for all $n \ge N$. Taking ε sufficiently small and setting $\nu = [- \log_\gamma \varepsilon]$ (largest integer less than or equal to $- \log_\gamma \varepsilon$), this means that the expansions of x and x_n in powers of π begin with the same power and agree up to the νth power.

On the other hand, let (x_n) be a Cauchy sequence of elements of K. This means that given any $\varepsilon > 0$, there exists an integer $N = N(\varepsilon)$ such that

$$|x_m - x_n| < \varepsilon$$

for all $m \geq N$ and $n \geq N$. Hence given any integer ν, putting $\varepsilon = \gamma^{-\nu}$, we see that all the terms in the sequence from the $N(\varepsilon)^{\underline{th}}$ term onward have the same expansion in powers of π up to the $\nu^{\underline{th}}$ power. If R is complete, the infinite expansion thus determined represents an element x of K which is clearly the limit of the sequence, hence K is complete. Conversely, given any infinite expansion in non-negative powers of π, truncating after the $n^{\underline{th}}$ power determines an element $x_n \in R$, and clearly the sequence (x_n) is a Cauchy sequence. Hence if K is complete, this expansion represents an element of R, so R is complete.

$\lrcorner$

(5.8) Note. While K is similar to the field $\mathbb{R}$ of real numbers in that it is a complete metric space, the geometry in K is quite different, because of the ultrametric inequality (5.5). For instance, every triangle in K is isosceles! Namely, given 3 points $x, y, z \in K$, we may assume that $z = 0$, say, and then if $|x| \neq |y|$, say $|x| < |y|$, we know that $|x - y| = |y|$. Moreover, every interval is both open and closed! This follows from the fact that the values of $|x|$ as x runs through K form a discrete subset of $\mathbb{R}$, namely

$$|x - a| < \gamma^{-n} \Leftrightarrow |x - a| \leq \gamma^{-(n+1)}$$

Note also that a necessary and sufficient condition for a sequence (x_n) in K to converge is that the sequence of absolute values of successive differences

$$|x_{n+1} - x_n|$$

converge to 0, as follows from the Cauchy criterion and the inequality

$$|x_{n+k} - x_n| \leq \max_{0 \leq j < k} \{|x_{n+j+1} - x_{n+j}|\}$$

Of course this condition is not sufficient for sequences of real numbers.

We now apply Newton's method to a polynomial f in one variable with coefficients in R to find a zero of f in R.

Consider first the derivative $\phi'(x)$ (5.2). For $x \in R$ we have

$$\left|\frac{f(x)f''(x)}{f'(x)^2}\right| = \left|\frac{f(x)}{f'(x)^2}\right| |f''(x)| \leq \left|\frac{f(x)}{f'(x)^2}\right|$$

since $f''(x) \in R$. This time we will need to bound $\left|\frac{f(x)}{f'(x)^2}\right|$ by a number less than 1, not merely bound $|\phi'(x)|$. It will suffice to bound it at one point in order to bound it over some interval (exercise -- we won't actually need this). Secondly, we will not need to assume ahead of time that f has a zero in the interval under consideration.

(5.9) HENSEL'S LEMMA. *Let* $a \in R$ *be such that* $f'(a) \neq 0$ *and*

$$\left|\frac{f(a)}{f'(a)^2}\right| < 1$$

Then the Newton sequence

$$a_{n+1} = a_n - \frac{f(a_n)}{f'(a_n)} \qquad n = 0,1,\ldots$$

which begins with $a_0 = a$ *converges to a zero* ξ *of* f. *This zero satisfies the inequality*

$$|\xi - a| < |f'(a)|$$

and is the only zero of f *satisfying that inequality*.

We cannot use the mean value theorem to prove this, as we did in the real case, since there is no notion of "betweenness" in K. We can, however, use the Taylor expansion of the polynomial f. The proof is clearer if we return to the valuation notation.

Let $\delta = v(f'(a))$. The hypothesis says

$$f(a) \equiv 0 \qquad (\text{mod } \pi^{2\delta+1})$$

so that dividing by $f'(a)^2$ gives an element of R satisfying

$$\frac{f(a)}{f'(a)^2} \equiv 0 \qquad (\text{mod } \pi)$$

We also have

$$a_1 \equiv a \qquad (\text{mod } \pi^{\delta+1})$$

We will show by induction that

(5.10) $$f(a_n) \equiv 0 \qquad (\text{mod } \pi^{2\delta+n+1})$$

(5.11) $$a_n \equiv a_{n-1} \qquad (\text{mod } \pi^{\delta+n})$$

which proves that (a_n) converges to a zero ξ of f such that

$$\xi \equiv a \qquad (\text{mod } \pi^{\delta+1})$$

Note first that (5.11) implies

$$f'(a_n) \equiv f'(a) \qquad (\text{mod } \pi^{\delta+1})$$

so that $v(f'(a_n)) = \delta$. Hence (5.10) gives

$$\frac{f(a_n)}{f'(a_n)} \equiv 0 \qquad (\text{mod } \pi^{\delta+n+1})$$

or in other words

$$a_{n+1} \equiv a_n \qquad (\text{mod } \pi^{\delta+n+1})$$

We then use the Taylor expansion

$$f(a_{n+1}) = f(a_n) - f'(a_n)\frac{f(a_n)}{f'(a_n)} + \left(\frac{f(a_n)}{f'(a_n)}\right)^2 c_n$$

where $c_n \in R$, so that actually we get the stronger congruence

$$f(a_{n+1}) \equiv 0 \pmod{\pi^{2\delta+2n+2}}$$

To prove uniqueness, suppose $f(\eta) = 0$ with

$$\eta \equiv a \pmod{\pi^{\delta+1}}$$

We will show by induction that

$$\eta \equiv a_n \pmod{\pi^{\delta+n+1}} \tag{5.12}$$

which proves that $\eta = \xi$.

Namely, the Taylor expansion gives

$$0 = f(\eta) = f(a_n) + f'(a_n)(\eta - a_n) + (\eta - a_n)^2 d_n$$

with $d_n \in R$. Since $v(f'(a_n)) = \delta$, dividing by $f'(a_n)$ and using (5.12) gives

$$\eta \equiv a_n - \frac{f(a_n)}{f'(a_n)} \pmod{\pi^{\delta+2n+2}}$$

a fortiori

$$\eta \equiv a_{n+1} \pmod{\pi^{\delta+n+2}}$$

⌟

(5.13) EXAMPLE. Consider the polynomial $f(X) = X^2 + 1$ over the ring $\underline{\underline{Z}}_p$, where p is odd. Then for any $a \in \underline{\underline{Z}}_p$ such that

$$a \not\equiv 0 \pmod{p}$$

we have

$$f'(a) = 2a \not\equiv 0 \pmod{p}$$

Thus Hensel's lemma tells us $\sqrt{-1}$ exists in $\underline{\underline{Z}}_p$ if and only if -1 is a quadratic residue mod p.

For instance,

$$2^2 \equiv -1 \pmod{5}$$

Taking the Newton sequence generated by a = 2 gives the 5-adic expansion of $\sqrt{-1}$. The first few terms are given as follows:

$$a_1 = a - \frac{f(a)}{f'(a)} = 2 - \frac{5}{4}$$

Since $4^2 \equiv 1 \pmod{5}$, and $-4 \equiv 1 \pmod{5}$,

$$a_1 \equiv 2 + 1 \cdot 5 \pmod{5^2}$$

To avoid fractions, we can start a new Newton sequence with $a_1 = 7$, so that

$$a_2 = a_1 - \frac{f(a_1)}{f'(a_1)} = 7 - \frac{25}{7}$$

Since $-\frac{1}{7} \equiv 2 \pmod 5$, we get

$$a_2 \equiv 2 + 1 \cdot 5 + 2 \cdot 5^2 \pmod{5^3}$$

etc. Thus once we have solved the congruence

$$x^2 \equiv -1 \pmod 5$$

the Newton sequence gives us solutions to the congruences

$$x^2 \equiv -1 \pmod{5^n}$$

for all n.

(5.14) EXAMPLE. Let p be any prime, and consider the polynomial $f(X) = X^{p-1} - 1$ over $\underline{\underline{Z}}_p$. For any $a \in \underline{\underline{Z}}_p$ not divisible by p, we have

$$f'(a) = (p-1)\, a^{p-2} \not\equiv 0 \pmod p$$

Hence there exists, by Hensel's lemma, a unique $(p-1)^{\underline{st}}$ root of unity in $\underline{\underline{Z}}_p$ which is congruent to a mod p. This determines an isomorphism of the multiplicative group of non-zero elements mod p onto the group of all $(p-1)^{\underline{st}}$ roots of unity. The latter group, together with the element 0, is called the set of multiplicative representatives of the residue field $\underline{\underline{Z}}/p$. We will generalize this construction in Chapter 6 to any complete discrete valuation ring of characteristic 0 whose residue field is a perfect field of characteristic p.

(5.15) EXAMPLE. Let $R = k[[T]]$, the power series ring in one variable over a field k. Let

$$f(X) = a_n(T)\ X^n + a_{n-1}(T)\ X^{n-1} + \cdots + a_1(T)\ X + a_0(T)$$

be a polynomial in a variable X whose coefficients are power series in T. We can consider f(X) as a function g(X, T) of two variables, substituting T = 0 gives a polynomial g(X, 0) with coefficients in k (g(X, 0) is the reduction of f(X) mod T). Suppose there exists $\alpha \in k$ such that

$$0 = g(\alpha, 0) = a_n(0)\ \alpha^n + \cdots + a_1(0)\ \alpha + a_0(0)$$

$$0 \neq \frac{\partial g}{\partial x}(\alpha, 0) = na_n(0)\ \alpha^{n-1} + \cdots + a_1(0)$$

so that α is a simple root of the polynomial g(X, 0). Hensel's Lemma then implies that there exists a unique power series $\xi(T) \in R$ such that

$$0 = f(\xi(T)) = a_n(T)\ \xi(T)^n + \cdots + a_1(T)\ \xi(T) + a_0(T)$$
$$\alpha = \xi(0)$$

This is an implicit function theorem for formal power series.

Note. If we take $k = \underline{\underline{C}}$, the field of complex numbers, and take R to be the subring of $\underline{\underline{C}}[[T]]$ consisting of those formal power series which actually converge in a neighborhood of zero, then the same result holds for this ring R, even though R is not complete, for it can be shown that R satisfies Hensel's Lemma, i.e., that the implicit function theorem for analytic functions holds.

As a special case of the above result, suppose a(T) is a power series whose constant term a(0) is not zero. Let m be a positive integer not divisible by the characteristic of k, and suppose a(0) has an $m^{\underline{th}}$ root α in k. Then there exists a formal power series b(T) such that

$$b(T)^m = a(T)$$

$$b(0) = \alpha$$

(apply the above result to $f(X) = X^m - a(T)$). There is nothing mysterious about this, since we can give an explicit formula for b(T). Namely, set

$$a(T) = a(0)(1 + c(T))$$

with $v(c(T)) \geq 1$. Then

$$b(T) = \alpha(1 + c(T))^{1/m}$$

where

$$(1 + c(T))^{1/m} = \sum_{n=0}^{\infty} \binom{1/m}{n} c(T)^n$$

(formal binomial series).

Here is another application.

(5.16) PROPOSITION. _Assume that the residue field_ k _of the complete discrete valuation ring_ R _has characteristic zero. Then_ R _contains a subfield isomorphic to_ k.

The proof is indirect, using Zorn's lemma.

Proof. Let $\phi: R \to k$ be the canonical homomorphism. For any integer $n \neq 0$, $\phi(n) \neq 0$ by hypothesis, so the non-zero integers are imbedded in the units of R and R contains the field $\underline{\underline{Q}}$ of all rational numbers. Now consider the non-empty set of all subfields of R, and order the elements of this set by inclusion. Applying Zorn's lemma gives a maximal subfield k_0 of R, and $\phi(k_0)$ is then a subfield of k isomorphic to k_0. We then have two cases to consider.

Case 1. k is a transcendental extension of $\phi(k_0)$, i.e., there exists an element $\tau \in k$ which satisfies no polynomial equation with coefficients in $\phi(k_0)$.

In that case choose any $t \in R$ such that $\phi(t) = \tau$. By hypothesis, all the non-zero elements of the algebra $k_0[t]$ generated by t over k_0 are units in R, so that the field $k_0(t)$ is contained in R. This is impossible because k_0 is maximal.

Case 2. k is an algebraic extension of $\phi(k_0)$.

Suppose there is an $\alpha \notin k$, with $\alpha \in \phi(k_0)$. Let

$$\bar{f}(X) = X^m + \phi(b_{m-1}) X^{m-1} + \cdots + \phi(b_0)$$

be the minimal polynomial of α over $\phi(k_0)$. Since k has characteristic zero, we have

$$0 \neq \bar{f}'(\alpha) = m\alpha^{m-1} + (m - 1) \phi(b_{m-1}) \alpha^{m-2} + \cdots + \phi(b_1)$$

Consider the polynomial

$$f(X) = X^m + b_{m-1} X^{m-1} + \cdots + b_0$$

with coefficients in k_0. By Hensel's Lemma, this polynomial has a root $a \in R$ such that $\phi(a) = \alpha$. Since $\bar{f}$ was irreducible, f is also, so that $k_0[a]$ is a subfield of R. This again contradicts the maximality of k_0.

Thus we have shown $\phi(k_0) = k$.

(5.17) Note. The conclusion of (5.16) holds for any complete discrete valuation R whose residue field has the same characteristic as R, but the proof requires some technique in characteristic p (see Theorem 27, p. 304, vol. 2 of [ZS]). The field of representatives k_0 is not, in general, uniquely determined.

(5.18) COROLLARY. *If the residue field* k *of the complete discrete valuation ring* R *has the same characteristic as* R, *then* R *is isomorphic to the formal power series ring* k[[T]].

We may assume, by (5.16) and (5.17), that $k \subset R$. Let π be a uniformizing parameter. Then R contains the ring $k[\pi]$ generated by π over k. If

$$f(\pi) = a_n\pi^n + \cdots + a_1\pi + a_0$$

is a polynomial in π with coefficients in k, and $a_n \neq 0$, then $v(f(\pi)) \leq n$, a fortiori, $f(\pi) \neq 0$. Thus $k[\pi]$ is isomorphic to the polynomial ring k[T] by an isomorphism leaving k fixed and sending π into T. Since R is complete, this isomorphism extends uniquely to an isomorphism of R with k[[T]].

⌟

In the next chapter we will discuss the structure of R when k is a *perfect* field of characteristic $p > 0$. If R also has characteristic p, then we will see that the field of representatives is unique. The other possibility is that R has characteristic zero, and we will then determine a multiplicative system of representatives (which do not form a field).

Our next task will be to generalize Hensel's Lemma in one variable (5.9) to several polynomials in more than one variable. We begin with the square case of n polynomials $f_1,\ldots,f_n$ in n variables $X_1,\ldots,X_n$. We will use vector notation as follows: Denote by

$$\underline{\underline{f}} = (f_1,\ldots,f_n)$$

the vector having these polynomials as components, and if $x = (x_1,\ldots,x_n) \in R^n$ is a vector with components in R, denote by $\underline{\underline{f}}(x)$ the vector

$$\underline{\underline{f}}(x) = (f_1(x),\ldots,f_n(x))$$

in R^n. We will need to consider the Jacobian matrix

$$M_{\underline{\underline{f}}} = (\partial f_i/\partial X_j)$$

and its determinant

$$J_{\underline{\underline{f}}} = \det(\partial f_i/\partial X_j)$$

If $x \in R^n$, it is clear what is meant by the matrix $M_{\underline{\underline{f}}}(x)$ and by its determinant $J_{\underline{\underline{f}}}(x) \in R$.

We will also need to consider vectors $\underline{\underline{f}}$ each of whose components is a formal power series in n variables over R. In that case $\underline{\underline{f}}(x)$ will not make sense for arbitrary $x \in R^n$ unless each of the series $f_i(x)$ converges. Certainly these series will converge if all the components of x are divisible by π (5.8). If $\underline{\underline{g}}$ is another vector of formal power series, we will further need to consider the composite series

$$\underline{\underline{f}} \circ \underline{\underline{g}} = \underline{\underline{f}}(\underline{\underline{g}})$$

obtained by substituting the series g_i for the variable X_i in $\underline{\underline{f}}$; once again, this need not make sense, but it will represent a uniquely determined system of power series if we know that $\underline{\underline{g}}$ is a system of series <u>without constant terms</u>, as is easily seen. A natural problem is to determine those systems $\underline{\underline{f}}$ which are invertible under this law of composition, i.e., for which there exists $\underline{\underline{g}}$ such that

$$\underline{\underline{f}} \circ \underline{\underline{g}} = X = \underline{\underline{g}} \circ \underline{\underline{f}}$$

where

$$X = (X_1, \ldots, X_n)$$

(5.19) PROPOSITION. <u>Let</u> $\underline{\underline{f}}$ <u>be a system of</u> n <u>formal series</u>

_in_ n _variables without constant term_. _Assume the Jacobian_ $J_{\underline{\underline{f}}}(0)$ _of_ $\underline{\underline{f}}$ _at the origin is a unit in the ring_ R. _Then_ $\underline{\underline{f}}$ _has an inverse system_ $\underline{\underline{g}}$ _which is uniquely determined_.

This proposition is valid over any commutative ring R, as the proof will show. Note that $J_{\underline{\underline{f}}}(0)$ is the determinant of the matrix (a_{ij}) where a_{ij} is the coefficient of X_j in the series f_i.

Proof. Introduce a new vector of variables $Y = (Y_1,\dots,Y_n)$. We wish to solve the system of equations

$$X_i = \sum_{j=1}^{n} a_{ij}Y_j + \sum_{\nu} a_{i\nu}Y^{\nu} \qquad (1 \le i \le n)$$

for Y, where in the second sum, all terms have degree = $\nu_1 + \dots + \nu_n$ at least 2, and where $\nu = (\nu_1,\dots,\nu_n)$,

$$Y^{\nu} = Y_1^{\nu_1}Y_2^{\nu_2} \cdots Y_n^{\nu_n}$$

By hypothesis the matrix $A = (a_{ij})$ has an inverse matrix $B = (b_{ij})$ with coefficients in R. Rewriting the above system of equations as one vector equation

$$X = \underline{\underline{f}}(Y)$$

operating on both sides with the matrix B gives an equivalent vector equation

$$Z = B\underline{\underline{f}}(Y)$$

where $Z = BX$, and where the coefficient of Y_j in the $i^{\underline{th}}$ component on the right is δ_{ij} (Kronecker delta). We may therefore assume

$$a_{ij} = \delta_{ij}$$

for all i,j, so that we must find a system $\underline{\underline{g}}$ in the variables X such that

$$X_i = g_i + \sum_{\nu} a_{i\nu} g_1^{\nu_1} \cdots g_n^{\nu_n} \qquad (1 \leq i \leq n)$$

From this it is obvious that the part of g_i of degree ≤ 1 must be simply X_i. Assume inductively that the sum h_{id} of the terms of degree $\leq d - 1$ in g_i has been determined for all i. Then the homogeneous part g_{id} of degree d in g_i is uniquely determined as being the homogeneous part of degree d in the series

$$-\sum_{\nu} a_{i\nu} h_{1d}^{\nu_1} \cdots h_{nd}^{\nu_n}$$

since the h_{id} have no constant terms. Thus $\underline{\underline{f}}$ has a uniquely determined right inverse $\underline{\underline{g}}$. Since we have

$$J_{\underline{\underline{g}}}(0) = J_{\underline{\underline{f}}}(0)^{-1}$$

the same argument shows $\underline{\underline{g}}$ has a right inverse $\underline{\underline{e}}$. But then

$$\underline{\underline{e}} = X \circ \underline{\underline{e}} = (\underline{\underline{f}} \circ \underline{\underline{g}}) \circ \underline{\underline{e}} = \underline{\underline{f}} \circ (\underline{\underline{g}} \circ \underline{\underline{e}}) = \underline{\underline{f}} \circ X = \underline{\underline{f}}$$

$\lrcorner$

We can now prove our square form of Hensel's Lemma.

(5.20) PROPOSITION. *Let* $\underline{\underline{f}}$ *be a system of* n *polynomials in* n *variables with coefficients in the complete discrete valuation ring* R. *Let* $a \in R^n$ *be such that*

$$\underline{\underline{f}}(a) \equiv 0 \qquad (\text{mod } \pi^{2\delta+1})$$

where

$$\delta = v(J_{\underline{\underline{f}}}(a)) < \infty$$

Then there exists a unique zero $b \in R^n$ *of the system* $\underline{\underline{f}}$ *such that*

$$b \equiv a \qquad (\text{mod } \pi^{\delta+1})$$

Proof. We will use the result from linear algebra that if N is the adjoint matrix of the matrix $M_{\underline{\underline{f}}}(a)$ we have

$$M_{\underline{\underline{f}}}(a)N = J_{\underline{\underline{f}}}(a)I$$

where I is the nxn identity matrix. By hypothesis,

$$J_{\mathbf{f}}(a) = u\pi^{\delta}$$

where u is a unit in R.

Taylor's formula applied to each of the polynomials in $\mathbf{f}$ gives the vector equation

$$\mathbf{f}(a + \pi^{\delta}X) = \mathbf{f}(a) + M_{\mathbf{f}}(a) \cdot \pi^{\delta}X + \pi^{2\delta}\mathbf{r}(X)$$

where $\mathbf{r}(X)$ is a vector of polynomials each of which begins with terms of degree ≥ 2. If $N' = u^{-1}N$, this formula can be rewritten as

$$\mathbf{f}(a + \pi^{\delta}X) = \mathbf{f}(a) + M_{\mathbf{f}}(a) \cdot \pi^{\delta}X + M_{\mathbf{f}}(a)N' \cdot \pi^{\delta}\mathbf{r}(X)$$

If we then set

$$\mathbf{g}(X) = X + N' \cdot \mathbf{r}(X)$$

we get

$$\mathbf{f}(a + \pi^{\delta}X) = \mathbf{f}(a) + M_{\mathbf{f}}(a) \cdot \pi^{\delta}\mathbf{g}(X)$$

We can then apply (5.19) to the system $\mathbf{g}$, which tells us there is a uniquely determined system $\mathbf{h}$ of formal power series without constant term inverse to the system (of polynomials) $\mathbf{g}$ under composition. Substituting $\mathbf{h}(X)$ for X in the above formula gives

$$\underline{\underline{f}}(a + \pi^{\delta}\underline{\underline{h}}(X)) = \underline{\underline{f}}(a) + M_{\underline{\underline{f}}}(a) \cdot \pi^{\delta}X$$

Into this formal identity we can substitute any vector $x \in R^n$ which is congruent to 0 mod π (since the series will then converge). By hypothesis

$$\underline{\underline{f}}(a) = \pi^{2\delta}c$$

where

$$c \equiv 0 \quad (\text{mod } \pi)$$

Hence we must find $x \equiv 0 \ (\text{mod } \pi)$ such that

$$0 = \pi^{2\delta}c + M_{\underline{\underline{f}}}(a) \cdot \pi^{\delta}x$$

or using the adjoint matrix again,

$$0 = \pi^{\delta}M_{\underline{\underline{f}}}(a) \cdot (N'c + x)$$

Since $M_{\underline{\underline{f}}}(a)$ is a non-singular matrix, this equation has the unique solution

$$x = -N'c \equiv 0 \quad (\text{mod } \pi)$$

Hence

$$b = \pi^{\delta}\underline{\underline{h}}(-N'c) + a$$

is the unique vector we have been looking for. ⌟

Note that, just as in the one variable case, the existence part of the proof is entirely constructive.

We now generalize the above result to a system of $n - r$ polynomials in n variables, $0 \le r < n$.

(5.21) GENERAL HENSEL LEMMA. *Let* $\underline{\underline{f}} = (f_{r+1}, \ldots, f_n)$ *be a system of* $n - r$ *polynomials in* n *variables over the complete discrete valuation ring* R. *Assume there exists* $a \in R^n$ *and an integer* $\delta > 0$ *such that*

$$\underline{\underline{f}}(a) \equiv 0 \pmod{\pi^{2\delta+1}}$$

and such that the Jacobian matrix $M_{\underline{\underline{f}}}(a)$ *reduced mod* $\pi^{\delta+1}$ *has maximal rank. Then there exists* $b \in R^n$ *which is a zero of* $\underline{\underline{f}}$ *such that*

$$b \equiv a \pmod{\pi^{\delta+1}}$$

Proof. We may assume that the particular determinant

$$D = \det(\partial f_i / \partial X_j) \qquad r + 1 \le i,j \le n$$

is not congruent to zero mod $\pi^{\delta+1}$. We expand our system to n polynomials by setting

$$f_i(X) = X_i - a_i$$

for $1 \le i \le r$. Then the Jacobian of the expanded system is equal to D, and we can apply the square form (5.20) of Hensel's lemma. ⌟

(5.22) Note. If $r > 0$ the solution b in (5.21) is not unique. We can, however, parametrize the set of solutions congruent to a mod $\pi^{\delta+1}$. Namely, in the notations of the proof of (5.20), it is clear that

$$g_i(X) = X_i = h_i(X) \qquad 1 \le i \le r$$

by definition of f_i for $1 \le i \le r$. Moreover, the matrix N' of that proof now has the form

$$\begin{pmatrix} \pi^{\delta} I_r & 0 \\ * & * \end{pmatrix}$$

so that for any vector x, the first r coordinates of N'x are $\pi^{\delta}x_1,\ldots,\pi^{\delta}x_r$.

In the identity

$$\underline{\underline{f}}(a + \pi^{\delta}\underline{\underline{h}}(X)) = \underline{\underline{f}}(a) + M_{\underline{\underline{f}}}(a) \cdot \pi^{\delta}X$$

let us substitute N'x for X, where $x \equiv 0 \pmod{\pi}$, so that we get

$$\begin{aligned} f_i(a_1 + \pi^{2\delta}x_1,\ldots,a_r + \pi^{2\delta}x_r, a_{r+1} + \pi^{\delta}h_{r+1}(N'x),\ldots,a_n + \pi^{\delta}h_n(N'x)) \\ = f_i(a_1,\ldots,a_n) + \pi^{2\delta}x_i \end{aligned}$$

for all $i = 1,\ldots,n$. By hypothesis,

$$f_j(a) = \pi^{2\delta} c_j$$

$$c_j \equiv 0 \pmod{\pi}$$

for $r + 1 \le j \le n$.

For any r-component vector $t = (t_1,\ldots,t_r)$, associate the n-component vector $x = (t_1,\ldots,t_r, -c_{r+1},\ldots, -c_n)$, and set

$$\phi_j(t) = h_j(N'x) \qquad r + 1 \le j \le n$$

Then for any $t \equiv 0 \pmod{\pi}$ we get

$$0 = f_j(a_1 + \pi^{2\delta}t_1,\ldots,a_r + \pi^{2\delta}t_r, a_{r+1} + \pi^{\delta}\phi_j(t),\ldots,a_n + \pi^{\delta}\phi_n(t))$$

for all $j = r + 1,\ldots,n$. This gives the parametrization. If I is the ideal in R generated by π, and $I^{\times r}$ is the set of all r-tuples taken from I, this parametrization gives a one-to-one analytic mapping of $I^{\times r}$ onto the set of all zeros of the unextended system $(f_{r+1},\ldots,f_n)$ which are congruent to a mod $\pi^{\delta+1}$ (geometrically, this means that in the neighborhood of a, the set of zeros forms an r-dimensional analytic manifold).

⌟

For future reference, we will repeat the statement of

Hensel's Lemma in case $r = n - 1$.

(5.23) COROLLARY. *Let* f *be a polynomial in* n *variables* $X_1,\ldots,X_n$ *over the complete discrete valuation ring* R. *Assume there exists* $a \in R^n$ *and an integer* $\delta > 0$ *such that*

$$f(a) \equiv 0 \pmod{\pi^{2\delta+1}}$$

and such that for some i,

$$\frac{\partial f}{\partial X_i}(a) \not\equiv 0 \pmod{\pi^{\delta+1}}$$

Then f *has a zero* $b \in R^n$ *such that*

$$b \equiv a \pmod{\pi^{\delta+1}}$$

The set of such zeros b *is parametrized by* $I^{\times(n-1)}$.

(5.24) *Note*. The above methods do not generalize to systems in which there are fewer variables than polynomials. There is a generalization of Hensel's Lemma to arbitrary systems $\underline{\underline{f}} = (f_1,\ldots,f_r)$ in n variables as follows: There exist integers $N \geq 1$, $c \geq 1$ and $s \geq 0$ depending on this system such that if $a \in R^n$ is such that

$$\underline{\underline{f}}(a) \equiv 0 \pmod{\pi^N}$$

then there exists a zero b of $\underline{\underline{f}}$ in R such that

$$b \equiv a \pmod{\pi^{[\frac{N}{c}]-s}}$$

(If the system is homogeneous and a is primitive, then the zero b is also primitive.) This is the result needed to prove (4.6) and (4.7) in the non-compact case. Here is a rough idea of the proof when R has characteristic zero:

The set of zeros of $\underline{\underline{f}}$ in the algebraic closure of the field K forms an algebraic variety V of a certain dimension m. The set of those zeros for which the Jacobian matrix does not have its maximal rank n - m is a subvariety S of V of lower dimension. (In case S is empty, i.e., V is non-singular, the integer c above can be taken to be 1.) The point is then that if we cannot arrange to satisfy the hypothesis of the General Hensel Lemma, we are reduced to solving the same problem for S instead of V, and since S has lower dimension, we can argue by induction. On the other hand, suppose we can find N so large that any $a \in R^n$ such that

$$\underline{\underline{f}}(a) \equiv 0 \pmod{\pi^N}$$

satisfies the Hensel hypothesis. In that case, (5.21) only assures us of refining a to a zero of n - m of the polynomials in $\underline{\underline{f}}$. Now the algebraic variety W defined by these n - m polynomials contains V as a component; let V' be the union of the other components. Then $V \cap V'$ is again a lower dimensional variety consisting of the zeros of $\underline{\underline{f}}$ and of some other system of polynomials $\underline{\underline{g}}$. If we cannot arrange to have $\underline{\underline{g}}(a) \not\equiv 0$ modulo a sufficiently high power of π, then by induction we can refine a to a zero in $V \cap V'$. For the details and for the case of characteristic p, see [Gb].

This result has recently been generalized by M. Artin from complete discrete valuation rings to higher dimensional complete local rings, with important applications in algebraic geometry.

CHAPTER 6

WITT VECTORS

Let k be a *perfect* field of characteristic $p > 0$ — this means that the one-to-one mapping $\alpha \to \alpha^p$ of k into itself is onto, hence an automorphism of k. The following result is due to Teichmüller.

(6.1) PROPOSITION. *If* R *is a complete discrete valuation ring whose residue field* k *is perfect of characteristic* p, *then* R *contains a unique system of multiplicative representatives of* k. *If* R *also has characteristic* p, *then these representatives form the unique subfield of* R *isomorphic to* k. *An element of* R *is the multiplicative representative of its residue class if and only if it has a* p^{n} *th root in* R *for all* $n \geq 1$.

Proof. We must show there is a unique one-to-one mapping

$$\alpha \to \{\alpha\}$$

of k into R such that

$$\{\alpha\beta\} = \{\alpha\}\{\beta\}$$

for all $\alpha, \beta \in k$. If R has characteristic p, we must also show

$$\{\alpha + \beta\} = \{\alpha\} + \{\beta\}$$

for all $\alpha, \beta \in k$. Let π be a uniformizing parameter in R. Since k has characteristic p, p must be divisible by π when R has characteristic zero. The key to our construction is the following lemma.

(6.2) LEMMA. _If_ $a \equiv b \pmod{\pi^i}$ _then_

$$a^{p^j} \equiv b^{p^j} \pmod{\pi^{i+j}}$$

The proof is by induction on j, the case $j = 0$ being our hypothesis. Let

$$b = a + \pi^i c, \quad c \in R$$

Then, by the binomial expansion,

$$b^p = a^p + p\pi^i cd + (\pi^i c)^p, \quad d \in R$$

since the intermediate terms have the form

$$\binom{p}{k} a^{p-k}(\pi^i c)^k$$

with binomial coefficients divisible by p. Hence

$$b^p \equiv a^p \pmod{\pi^{i+1}}$$

and we are done by induction. (If R has characteristic p, a sharper congruence can be obtained, but never mind.) ⌟

Given $\alpha \in k$. For each non-negative integer n, let $a_n \in R$ be a representative of $\alpha^{p^{-n}} \in k$. Consider the sequence $(a_0, a_1^p, a_2^{p^2}, \ldots, a_n^{p^n}, \ldots)$. Each term in the sequence is a representative of α. Moreover, we have

$$a_{n+1}^p \equiv a_n \pmod{\pi}$$

so that by the lemma

$$(a_{n+1})^{p^{n+1}} \equiv a_n^{p^n} \pmod{\pi^{n+1}}$$

It follows that the sequence converges to an element in R. I claim that the limit depends only on α. Indeed, if

$$b_n \equiv a_n \pmod{\pi}$$

then by the lemma

$$b_n^{p^n} \equiv a_n^{p^n} \pmod{\pi^{n+1}}$$

Denote the limit by $\{\alpha\}$. Note that if a_0 had a p^n th root

a_n in R for all n, then making this choice would have given us the constant sequence $(a_0, a_0, a_0, \ldots)$, so that $a_0 = \{\alpha\}$. In any case, it is clear that

$$a_0 \equiv \{\alpha\} \pmod{\pi}$$

so that $\{\alpha\}$ is indeed a representative of α.

Given α, $\beta \in k$, let $(a_n^{p^n})$, $(b_n^{p^n})$ be sequences converging to $\{\alpha\}$, $\{\beta\}$, respectively. Since $(xy)^p = x^p y^p$ no matter what the characteristic of R, it is clear from the convergence of $(a_n^{p^n} b_n^{p^n})$ to $\{\alpha\}\{\beta\}$ that

$$\{\alpha\}\{\beta\} = \{\alpha\beta\}$$

On the other hand, if R has characteristic p, we also have

$$a_n^{p^n} + b_n^{p^n} = (a_n + b_n)^{p^n}$$

so that

$$\{\alpha\} + \{\beta\} = \{\alpha + \beta\}$$

and the representatives form a subfield.

Finally, suppose $\alpha \to [\alpha]$ were another multiplicative system of representatives. Then, as we have seen,

$$[\alpha] = [\alpha^{1/p^n}]^{p^n} \equiv \{\alpha\} \pmod{\pi^{n+1}}$$

for all n, hence $[\alpha] = \{\alpha\}$. ⌟

We will continue to use the notation $\{\alpha\}$ of the previous proof. We have already seen (5.18) that if R has characteristic p then R is isomorphic to the power series ring in one variable over k. We assume henceforth R has characteristic zero. We know every $a \in R$ has a unique representation

$$a = \{\alpha_0\} + \{\alpha_1\}\pi + \cdots + \{\alpha_n\}\pi^n + \cdots$$

but we do not know how to add or multiply these expressions as yet.

We know that p is divisible by π,

$$p = u\pi^e$$

where u is a unit in R and $e = v(p)$. In case $e = 1$ we say that R is unramified; in that case, since the choice of uniformizing parameter π was arbitrary, we will make the canonical choice $\pi = p$, so that a typical element $a \in R$ has the representation

$$a = \{\alpha_0\} + \{\alpha_1\}p + \cdots + \{\alpha_n\}p^n + \cdots$$

For example, $\mathbb{Z}_p$ is unramified, but note that the multiplicative representatives are not the ordinary integers $0,1,\dots,p-1$ (e.g., see (5.13) for the case $p = 5$).

Assume now R is unramified. We will show that the ring operations in R are uniquely determined by those in k. In fact, the whole structure of R is determined by the formula

$$\{\alpha\} + \{\beta\} = \sum_{n=0}^{\infty} \{s_n(\alpha,\beta)\}p^n$$

where $s_n(\alpha,\beta) \in k$ must be determined for all n (clearly $s_0(\alpha,\beta) = \alpha + \beta$). We will show this by induction. Assume the structure of the residue ring R/p^n has been determined (i.e., that we know all the ring operations modulo p^n). We will determine the structure of R/p^{n+1}.

We first compute $-\{\alpha\} \in R$. If p is odd, then the multiplicative representative of $-1 \in k$ is $-1 \in R$; namely if $a_n \in R$ is such that

$$a_n^{p^n} = 1$$

then

$$(-a_n)^{p^n} = -1$$

Hence if p is odd

$$-\{\alpha\} = \{-1\}\{\alpha\} = \{-\alpha\}$$

However, if $p = 2$, -1 has the 2-adic expansion

$$-1 = \frac{1}{1-2} = 1 + 2 + 2^2 + \cdots + 2^n + \cdots$$

Hence

$$-\{\alpha\} = (-1)\{\alpha\} = \{\alpha\} + \{\alpha\}2 + \{\alpha\}2^2 + \cdots + \{\alpha\}2^n + \cdots$$

Next, we determine explicitly the structure of R/p^2.

Let

$$a = \{\alpha_0\} + \{\alpha_1\}p$$

$$b = \{\beta_0\} + \{\beta_1\}p$$

Multiplying,

$$ab \equiv \{\alpha_0\beta_0\} + (\{\alpha_0\beta_1\} + \{\alpha_1\beta_0\})p \pmod{p^2}$$

Since

$$\{\alpha_0\beta_1\} + \{\alpha_1\beta_0\} \equiv \{\alpha_0\beta_1 + \alpha_1\beta_0\} \pmod{p}$$

we have

$$ab \equiv \{\alpha_0\beta_0\} + \{\alpha_0\beta_1 + \alpha_1\beta_0\}p \pmod{p^2}$$

This looks just like $k[T]/T^2$. However, adding gives

$$a + b = \{\alpha_0\} + \{\beta_0\} + (\{\alpha_1\} + \{\beta_1\})p$$

Now

$$\{\alpha_0\} + \{\beta_0\} \equiv \{\alpha_0 + \beta_0\} + \{s_1(\alpha_0, \beta_0)\}p \pmod{p^2}$$

hence

$$a + b \equiv \{\alpha_0 + \beta_0\} + \{\alpha_1 + \beta_1 + s_1(\alpha_0, \beta_0)\}p \pmod{p^2}$$

which shows that the formula for $a + b$ will be known as soon as we determine $s_1(\alpha_0, \beta_0)$.

Since k is perfect, we can take $p^{\underline{th}}$ roots. Then $\{\alpha_0^{1/p}\} + \{\beta_0^{1/p}\}$ is a representative of $\alpha_0^{1/p} + \beta_0^{1/p}$, so that

$$\{\alpha_0^{1/p}\} + \{\beta_0^{1/p}\} \equiv \{\alpha_0^{1/p} + \beta_0^{1/p}\} \pmod{p}$$

Raising both sides to the $p^{\underline{th}}$ power gives

$$(\{\alpha_0^{1/p}\} + \{\beta_0^{1/p}\})^p \equiv \{\alpha_0 + \beta_0\} \pmod{p^2}$$

Expanding the left side by the binomial theorem gives

$$\{\alpha_0\} + \{\beta_0\} + \sum_{k=1}^{p-1} \binom{p}{k} \{\alpha_0^{(p-k)/p} \beta_0^{k/p}\}$$

If we factor p out of the binomial coefficients, we get a polynomial in $\{\alpha_0^{1/p}\}$ and $\{\beta_0^{1/p}\}$ with integer coefficients. Thus

$$s_1(\alpha_0, \beta_0) = -\sum_{k=1}^{p-1} \frac{1}{p}\binom{p}{k}\alpha_0^{(p-k)/p}\beta_0^{k/p}$$

Finally, assume the structure of R/p^n known. Let

$$a = \sum_{i=0}^{n} \{\alpha_i\}p^i$$

$$b = \sum_{i=0}^{n} \{\beta_i\}p^i$$

Then

$$ab = \sum_{k=0}^{n} (\sum_{i+j=k} \{\alpha_i\beta_j\})p^k$$

For $k \geq 1$, the p-adic expansion of

$$\sum_{i+j=k} \{\alpha_i\beta_j\}$$

need only be determined up to the coefficient of p^{n-k}; since the structure of R/p^n is given, this expansion is known. For $k = 0$ we have $\{\alpha_0\beta_0\}$. Thus multiplication in R/p^{n+1} is determined by addition. As for addition,

$$a + b = \sum_{i=0}^{n} (\{\alpha_i\} + \{\beta_i\})p^i$$

For $i \geq 1$, the p-adic expansion of $\{\alpha_i\} + \{\beta_i\}$ need only be determined up to the coefficient of p^{n-1}, hence is known. Thus $a + b$ will be determined once we know the coefficient of p^n in the expansion of $\{\alpha_0\} + \{\beta_0\}$.

Dropping the subscript 0, we have by (6.2)

$$(\{\alpha^{p^{-n}}\} + \{\beta^{p^{-n}}\})^{p^n} \equiv \{\alpha + \beta\} \pmod{p^{n+1}}$$

Expanding the left side by the binomial theorem gives

$$\{\alpha\} + \{\beta\} + \sum_{k=1}^{p^n-1} \binom{p^n}{k} \{\alpha^{1-kp^{-n}} \beta^{kp^{-n}}\}$$

Since p divides all the binomial coefficients, we can factor it out and are left with a polynomial in $\{\alpha^{p^{-n}}\}$ and $\{\beta^{p^{-n}}\}$ with integer coefficients. We can (by inductive hypothesis) determine the p-adic expansion of this polynomial up to the coefficient of p^{n-1}. Bringing that term over to the right side (which introduces the minus signs) we ultimately obtain the p-adic expansion of $\{\alpha\} + \{\beta\}$ up to the coefficient of p^n. We thus have the following theorem .

(6.3) THEOREM. _Let R_1, R_2 be complete discrete unramified valuation rings of characteristic zero having the same perfect residue field k of characteristic $p > 0$. Then there is a unique isomorphism of R_1 with R_2 inducing the identity on_ k.

Proof. From the argument above, the mapping given by

$$\sum_{n=0}^{\infty} \{\alpha_n\}_1 p^n \to \sum_{n=0}^{\infty} \{\alpha_n\}_2 p^n$$

where $\{\alpha\}_i$ is the multiplicative representative of $\alpha \in k$ in the ring R_i, $i = 1,2$, is the unique isomorphism.

Having established uniqueness, we now ask whether there exists a complete discrete unramified valuation ring R of characteristic zero having a given perfect residue field k of characteristic p. The construction is due to E. Witt (1936) and gives an alternative method of computing the addition and multiplication in R.

Let $X_1, X_2, \ldots$ be a sequence of indeterminates. For any positive integer n, set

$$X^{(n)} = \sum_{d|n} dX_d^{n/d} \tag{6.4}$$

(so that $X^{(1)} = X_1$, $X^{(2)} = X_1^2 + 2X_2$, $X^{(4)} = X_1^4 + 2X_2^2 + 4X_4$, etc.). These polynomials will be called the ghost components of the vector $X = (X_1, X_2, \ldots)$. The sequence of ghost components determines X uniquely, since by induction we can show that X_n is a polynomial with rational coefficients in the ghost components $X^{(d)}$ where d runs through the divisors of n.

The ghost components appear as follows: Let T be

another indeterminate, and consider the power series given in formal product form by

$$(6.5) \qquad f_X(T) = \prod_{n\geq 1} (1 - X_n T^n)$$

(6.6) PROPOSITION. _The ghost components satisfy_

$$-T \frac{d}{dT} \log f_X(T) = \sum_{n\geq 1} X^{(n)} T^n$$

where the logarithmic derivative on the left is taken formally.

Proof.

$$\log f_X(T) = \sum_{n\geq 1} \log (1 - X_n T^n)$$

$$\frac{d}{dT} \log f_X(T) = \sum_{n\geq 1} \frac{-nX_n T^{n-1}}{1 - X_n T^n}$$

$$= \sum_{n\geq 1} -nX_n T^{n-1} (1 + (X_n T^n) + (X_n T^n)^2 + \ldots)$$

$$-T \frac{d}{dT} \log f_X(T) = \sum_{n\geq 1} n \sum_{k\geq 1} (X_n T^n)^k$$

The proposition is now easily verified by examining the coefficient of a given power of T. ┘

Let $Y = (Y_1, Y_2, \ldots)$ be another infinite vector of indeterminates. We define the _Witt sum and product_ of X and Y by the formulas

$$(X \dotplus Y)^{(n)} = X^{(n)} \dotplus Y^{(n)} \tag{6.7}$$

In words: Add (resp. multiply) the $n^{\underline{th}}$ ghost component of X to (resp. with) the $n^{\underline{th}}$ ghost component of Y. This new sequence of components is to be the sequence of ghost components of a uniquely determined vector called the Witt sum (resp. Witt product) of X and Y. A priori, the components of $X \dotplus Y$ will be given by polynomials in the components of X and Y with rational coefficients. However, more is true.

(6.8) THEOREM. $(X \dotplus Y)_n$ <u>is a polynomial in</u> $X_1, Y_1, \ldots, X_n, Y_n$ <u>having integer coefficients.</u>

The proof follows immediately from the formulas

$$f_X(T) f_Y(T) = f_{X+Y}(T) \tag{6.9}$$

$$f_{XY}(T) = \prod_{d,e\geq 1} (1 - X_d^{m/d} Y_e^{m/e} T^m)^{de/m} \tag{6.10}$$

where in (6.10) m is the least common multiple of d,e.

To demonstrate these formulas, note that (6.6) and the definition of $X + Y$ give

$$\frac{d}{dT} \log f_{X+Y}(T) = \frac{d}{dT} (\log f_X(T) + \log f_Y(T))$$

Integrating formally (and noting that the constant terms agree), we get

$$\log f_{X+Y}(T) = \log f_X(T) + \log f_Y(T)$$

so that (6.9) follows from the properties of the logarithm.

As for (6.10), let g(T) denote the right side. Then

$$\log g(T) = \sum_{d,e\geq 1} \frac{de}{m} \log (1 - X_d^{m/d} Y_e^{m/e} T^m)$$

$$-T \frac{d}{dT} \log g(T) = \sum_{d,e\geq 1} de \frac{X_d^{m/d} Y_e^{m/e} T^m}{1 - X_d^{m/d} Y_e^{m/e} T^m}$$

$$= \sum_{d,e\geq 1} de \sum_{k\geq 1} X_d^{km/d} Y_e^{km/e} T^{km}$$

Keeping in mind that $m = \text{lcm}(d,e)$, it is easily seen that the coefficient of T^n in this series is just $X^{(n)}Y^{(n)}$; formula (6.10) then follows by integrating and exponentiating.

∎

Now let p be a prime number. <u>We will only consider components indexed by a power of</u> p, <u>i.e., we will only consider vectors whose other components are equal to zero.</u> We can therefore simplify our notation and write X_n instead of X_{p^n}. The same notational change applies to the ghost components, so that we now have

$$(6.11) \qquad X^{(n)} = X_0^{p^n} + pX_1^{p^{n-1}} + \ldots + p^n X_n$$

for all $n \geq 0$.

Let k be a field of characteristic $p > 0$.

(6.12) DEFINITION. <u>The ring</u> $W(k)$ <u>of Witt vectors with components in</u> k <u>consists of all infinite vectors</u>

$$x = (x_0, x_1, \ldots), \quad \text{all } x_i \in k$$

<u>with the Witt sum and product</u> (6.7).

In making this definition, we are using Theorem (6.8), for the coefficients of the polynomials giving the sum and product are meaningful mod p only because they are integers.

(6.13) EXAMPLE. Let us find the first few components of $-x$. Clearly $(-x)_0 = -x_0$. We will use our indeterminates and work in characteristic zero. Let $Y = -X$. We know $Y_0 = -X_0$. Since $Y^{(1)} = -X^{(1)}$, we have (using 6.11)

$$(-X_0)^p + pY_1 = -X_0^p - pX_1$$

If p is odd, we can cancel $-X_0^p$ from both sides, obtaining $Y_1 = -X_1$. If $p = 2$, however, we get $Y_1 = -X_0^2 - X_1$. Using the fact that $-1 \equiv +1 \pmod 2$, we obtain finally

$$(-x)_1 = \begin{cases} -x_1 & p \text{ odd} \\ x_1 + x_0^2 & p = 2 \end{cases}$$

In fact it is easily seen that

$$(-x)_n = -x_n$$

for all n when p is odd, but for $p = 2$ the formula for $(-x)_n$ is more complicated. For the particular vector $x = (x_0, 0, 0, \ldots)$ it can easily be seen that

$$-x = (x_0, x_0^2, x_0^4, \ldots, x_0^{2^n}, \ldots)$$

when $p = 2$.

REMARK. One property of the Witt polynomials which is important for certain applications is expressed by the formulas

$$(6.14) \qquad (x + y)_n = x_n + y_n + A_n(x_0, \ldots, x_{n-1}; y_0, \ldots, y_{n-1})$$

$$(6.15) \qquad (xy)_n = x_0^{p^n} y_n + y_0^{p^n} x_n + M_n(x_0, \ldots, x_{n-1}; y_0, \ldots, y_{n-1})$$

where A_n and M_n are polynomials not involving x_n and y_n (exercise).

We now define two important operators V and F on Witt vectors by

(6.16) $$VX = (0, X_0, X_1, \ldots)$$

(6.17) $$FX = (X_0^p, X_1^p, \ldots)$$

Thus V shifts one notch to the right, inserting a zero at the beginning. Clearly these operators commute. In terms of the ghost components we have

(6.18) $$(VX)^{(n)} = pX^{(n-1)}$$

(6.19) $$X^{(n)} = (FX)^{(n-1)} + p^n X_n$$

for all $n \geq 1$, as follows immediately from the definitions.

(6.20) PROPOSITION. *Let* k *be a perfect field of characteristic* p. *Then the shift operator* V *is an additive endomorphism of* W(k) *and the Frobenius operator* F *is a ring automorphism of* W(k). *Furthermore,*

$$px = VFx = (0, x_0^p, x_1^p, \ldots)$$

for all $x \in W(k)$.

Proof. That V is additive follows at once from (6.18). That F is both multiplicative and additive follows from the fact that the Witt polynomials P have coefficients in the prime field mod p, so that they satisfy

$$P(x_0^p, \ldots, x_n^p; y_0^p, \ldots, y_n^p) = P(x_0, \ldots, x_n; y_0, \ldots, y_n)^p$$

F is certainly one-to-one, and it is onto by our hypothesis that k is perfect.

Let us restate the last part of the proposition. Let Y be the vector obtained by Witt-adding X to itself p times. We wish to show

$$Y_n \equiv (VFX)_n \pmod{p}$$

for all n. By definition we have

$$Y^{(n)} = pX^{(n)}$$

for all n. For n = 0 this gives

$$Y_0 \equiv 0 \pmod{p}$$

For $n \geq 1$, formulas (6.18) and (6.19) give

$$\begin{aligned}(FY)^{(n-1)} + p^n Y_n &= Y^{(n)} = pX^{(n)} \\ &= (VX)^{(n+1)} \\ &= (FVX)^{(n)} + p^{n+1}(VX)_{n+1} \\ &= (FFVX)^{(n-1)} + p^n(FVX)_n + p^{n+1}(VX)_{n+1}\end{aligned}$$

By inductive hypothesis, we have

$$Y_j \equiv (FVX)_j \qquad (\text{mod } p)$$

for all $j < n$, and raising to the $p^{\underline{th}}$ power gives

$$(FY)_j \equiv (FFVX)_j \qquad (\text{mod } p^2)$$

for all $j < n$. Using lemma (6.2) and the definition of the ghost components (6.11), these congruences imply the congruence

$$(FY)^{(n-1)} \equiv (FFVX)^{(n-1)} \qquad (\text{mod } p^{n+1})$$

Substituting this into the previous equation gives

$$p^n Y_n \equiv p^n (FVX)_n \qquad (\text{mod } p^{n+1})$$

so that dividing by p^n gives the congruence we want. ⌟

(6.21) COROLLARY. W(k) <u>has characteristic zero and its residue ring mod</u> p <u>is canonically isomorphic to</u> k .

<u>Proof.</u> For any n, the Witt vector p^n has a 1 in the $n^{\underline{th}}$ place and 0 in every other place, a fortiori $p^n \neq 0$. Since k is perfect, (6.20) implies that the ideal generated by p consists of those vectors x with $x_0 = 0$. Hence the residue ring mod p is isomorphic to k by the isomorphism induced

from the homomorphism $x \to x_0$. It follows that W(k) must have characteristic zero. ┘

We now define a valuation v on W(k) by $v(x) = n$ provided $x_n \neq 0$, and $x_j = 0$ for all $j < n$. Equivalently, $v(x) = n$ provided that

$$x = up^n$$

where $u_0 \neq 0$. Since p generates a maximal ideal in W(k) (6.21), u is a unit. It follows that W(k) is a discrete valuation ring under v. Since $v(p) = 1$, W(k) is unramified.

The residue ring of W(k) modulo p^{n+1} is canonically isomorphic to the ring $W_n(k)$ obtained by truncating all Witt vectors after the $n^{\underline{th}}$ component. Clearly we have a canonical isomorphism

$$W(k) \cong \varprojlim_n W_n(k)$$

so that W(k) is complete.

We summarize our results.

(6.22) THEOREM. Let k be a perfect field of characteristic p. Then W(k) is a complete discrete unramified valuation ring

<u>of characteristic zero with residue field</u> k.

To conclude our discussion, note that the multiplicative representative $\{\alpha\}$ of $\alpha \in k$ in W(k) is the Witt vector $(\alpha, 0, 0, \ldots)$ (as follows easily from the definition of Witt multiplication). Then

$$\{\alpha\}p = (0, \alpha^p, 0, 0, \ldots)$$

$$\{\alpha\}p^2 = (0, 0, \alpha^{p^2}, 0, 0, \ldots)$$

etc., by (6.20). One can then show, using the definition of Witt addition, that the p-adic expansion of a Witt vector $x = (x_0, x_1, \ldots)$ is given by

$$x = \sum_{n=0}^{\infty} \{x_n^{p^{-n}}\}p^n \qquad (6.23)$$

This explains why the formulas for addition and multiplication of Witt vectors do not involve p^{th} roots as do the formulas for addition and multiplication in terms of the coefficients in the p-adic expansion.

We must next discuss the structure of R in the ramified case.

Let e be the <u>ramification index</u> of R, so that

$$p = u\pi^e$$

with u a unit in R, π a uniformizing parameter.

Within R, it makes sense to consider the set of all power series of the form

$$\sum_{n=0}^{\infty} \{\alpha_n\} p^n$$

This set forms a subring S of R which is a complete discrete unramified valuation ring with the same residue field k (note, however, that the valuation w on S is not the restriction of the valuation v on R, since $w(p) = 1$, $v(p) = e$).

Given $a \in R$. Since S has the same residue field as R, there exists $s_0 \in S$ such that

$$a = s_0 + a_1\pi , \quad a_1 \in R$$

Applying the same argument to a_1, we get

$$a_1 = s_1 + a_2\pi, \quad s_1 \in S, \quad a_2 \in R$$

$$a = s_0 + s_1\pi + a_2\pi^2$$

Continuing in this way, we get after e steps

$$a = s_0 + s_1\pi + \ldots + s_{e-1}\pi^{e-1} + a_e\pi^e$$

with $s_0, \ldots, s_{e-1} \in S$, $a_e \in R$. Replacing π^e by $u^{-1}p$, this can be written

$$a = s_0 + s_1\pi + \ldots + s_{e-1}\pi^{e-1} + a^{(1)}p$$

with $a^{(1)} \in R$. We can then apply the same process to $a^{(1)}$.

$$a^{(1)} = s_0^{(1)} + s_1^{(1)}\pi + \ldots + s_{e-1}^{(1)}\pi^{e-1} + a^{(2)}p$$

$$a = (s_0 + s_0^{(1)}p) + (s_1 + s_1^{(1)}p)\pi + \ldots + (s_{e-1} + s_{e-1}^{(1)}p)\pi^{e-1} + a^{(2)}p^2$$

Continuing in this way, each of the series

$$s_j + \sum_{k=1}^{\infty} s_j^{(k)}p^k$$

will converge to an element $t_j \in S$ and we will have

$$a = t_0 + t_1\pi + \ldots + t_{e-1}\pi^{e-1}$$

We have thus proved

(6.24) PROPOSITION. R _is a finitely generated module over_ S, _generated by_ $1, \pi, \ldots, \pi^{e-1}$.

It can be shown that π can be chosen to satisfy an Eisenstein equation

$$\pi^e + s_1\pi^{e-1} + \ldots + s_e = 0$$

where the $s_i \in S$ are all divisible by p, but s_e not

divisible by p^2 [S]. We will not need this fact.

We can now apply the Witt polynomials to prove the following theorem.

(6.25) THEOREM (Lang). _Let_ R _be a complete discrete valuation ring with residue field_ k _and field of fractions_ K. _If_ k _is algebraically closed then_ K _is_ C_1 . _In particular, there are no central division algebras over_ K.

Proof. By (5.18) (and (6.1)), if R has the same characteristic as k then R is isomorphic to the power series ring k[[T]]. In that case the theorem is a special case of (4.8).

Assume now k has characteristic $p > 0$ while R has characteristic zero. Then R may be ramified, but in that case K is a finite extension field of the field of fractions of the unramified subring of R having the same residue field k (6.24). Hence (3.5) it suffices to prove the theorem in the case R is unramified.

In that case, R is canonically isomorphic to W(k) (6.3), say $R = W(k)$.

Let f be a homogeneous polynomial of degree d in n variables over R, with $n > d$. By (4.7), we must show that f has a primitive zero in

$$W_m(k) = R/p^{m+1}$$

for all $m \geq 0$. In any solution

$$f(x) = f(x_1, \ldots, x_n) = 0 \quad \text{all } x_i \in W_n(k)$$

each x_i is a Witt vector of length $m + 1$:

$$x_i = (\xi_{i0}, \xi_{i1}, \ldots, \xi_{im}) \qquad 1 \leq i \leq n$$

On the other hand, whether or not it is equal to zero, $f(x)$ is again a Witt vector $(f_0, f_1, \ldots, f_m)$. Its components depend on the ξ_{ij} , of course, but we can be even more specific. Since the addition and multiplication in $W_m(k)$ are given by polynomial formulas (with coefficients in k) in the component variables, the components $f_0, \ldots, f_m$ of $f(x)$ are polynomials in the ξ_{ij}. In fact (6.8), f_i is a polynomial depending only on the first $(i + 1)$ columns of the matrix x, i.e., if $\xi_j = (\xi_{1j}, \xi_{2j}, \ldots, \xi_{nj})$, then

$$f_i = f_i(\xi_0, \ldots, \xi_i)$$

Finding a primitive zero of f in $W_m(k)$ is thus equivalent to finding a common zero ξ in k of the polynomials $f_0, f_1, \ldots, f_m$ such that the vector ξ_0 is not zero. The total number of variables in ξ is $n(m + 1)$.

Suppose the solution x in $W_m(k)$ is not primitive,

so that $\xi_0 = 0$. Then for all i, $1 \le i \le n$, we have

$$x_i = py_i$$

where

$$y_i = (\eta_{i0}, \ldots, \eta_{im})$$

$$\xi_{i1} = \eta_{i0}^p, \ldots, \xi_{im} = \eta_{im-1}^p$$

Then $0 = f(x) = f(py) = p^d f(y)$. Now multiplication by p^d shifts a Witt vector d places to the right and raises all components to the p^d th power (6.20). Hence

(a) $f_i(0, \xi_1, \ldots, \xi_i) = 0$ if $i < d$

(b) $f_i(0, \xi_1, \ldots, \xi_i) = f_{i-d}^{p^d}(\xi_1^{p^{d-1}}, \ldots, \xi_{i-d+1}^{p^{d-1}})$ if $i \ge d$

where $f_{i-d}^{p^d}$ means that the coefficients of f_{i-d} are to be raised to the p^d th power.

We now argue by contradiction. Suppose that for some m, all the zeros of f in $W_m(k)$ are non-primitive. Then the same is true for $W_r(k)$ for all $r \ge m$, in particular for $r = m + d$. Thus finding a zero of f in $W_{m+d}(k)$ amounts to solving the system

$$f_0(0) = 0, f_1(0, \xi_1) = 0, \ldots, f_{m+d}(0, \xi_1, \ldots, \xi_{m+d}) = 0$$

which by (b) above is equivalent to solving the system

$$f_0(\xi_1) = 0,\ f_1(\xi_1, \xi_2) = 0, \ldots, f_m(\xi_1, \ldots, \xi_{m+1}) = 0$$

(the $p^{\underline{th}}$ powers can be ignored). By assumption, this system has all solutions satisfying $\xi_1 = 0$. Continuing this argument, we see that the system $f_0 = 0, \ldots, f_{m+kd} = 0$ has all solutions satisfying $\xi_0 = \xi_1 = \ldots = \xi_k = 0$.

Consider now the dimension of the variety of zeros of the system $f_0 = 0, \ldots, f_{m+kd} = 0$ in the space of $n(m + kd + 1)$ variables. Since k is algebraically closed, this (affine) variety has dimension at least

$$n(m + kd + 1) - (m + kd + 1)$$

(see [Lg 1]) but by the previous paragraph, its dimension is at most

$$n(m + kd + 1) - n(k + 1)$$

Comparing these two numbers, we get

$$(n - d)k \leq m + 1 - n$$

for all k, which contradicts $n > d$. Hence f has a primitive zero in $W_m(k)$. ⌟

REMARK. One might try to generalize the above argument to the case where k is assumed C_i, $i > 0$, and try to prove K is C_{i+1}. The trouble is then that one has to keep track of the degrees of the polynomials $f_0, \ldots, f_m$, and in fact these degrees go up very fast with m. Indeed, we will see in the next chapter that when k is C_1 and R has characteristic different from that of k then K need not be C_2.

(6.26) NOTE. Let us examine the field K of the previous theorem in the case where k is the algebraic closure of the prime field $\mathbb{Z}/p$ and R **is** unramified. Then $\mathbb{Q}_p \subset K$ (since $\mathbb{Z}_p = W(\mathbb{Z}/p) \subset W(k) = R$). Let k_m be the finite field with p^m elements, K_m the field of fractions of $W(k_m)$. Then

$$k = \bigcup_{m=1}^{\infty} k_m$$

The field k_m is the splitting field over $\mathbb{Z}/p$ of the polynomial $X^{p^m} - 1$ and its multiplicative group is generated by a primitive p^m th root of unity ξ_m. The multiplicative representatives of k_m in $W(k_m)$ consist, then, of zero and all the p^m th roots of unity over $\mathbb{Q}_p$. It follows that $K_m = \mathbb{Q}_p(\{\xi_m\})$. The field

$$K_\infty = \bigcup_{m=1}^{\infty} K_m$$

is the maximal unramified algebraic extension of $\mathbb{Q}_p$; it is the field of fractions of the ring

$$R_\infty = \bigcup_{m=1}^{\infty} W(k_m)$$

Since the Witt vector

$$\xi = (\xi_1, \xi_2, \ldots, \xi_m, \ldots)$$

does not belong to R_∞, R_∞ is not complete; but we obviously have

$$R_\infty / p^{\nu+1} = W_\nu(k) \qquad \text{(for all } \nu\text{)}$$

so that $W(k)$ is the completion of R_∞.

The field k, being algebraically closed, contains all the roots of unity. Let q be a prime different from p, r any positive integer. The primitive q^r th root of unity over $\underline{\underline{Z}}/p$ lies in some k_m, hence its multiplicative representative in $W(k_m)$ is a primitive q^r th root of unity over $\underline{\underline{Q}}_p$. It follows that K_∞ contains all the roots of unity over $\underline{\underline{Q}}_p$, so that K_∞ is the cyclotomic extension of $\underline{\underline{Q}}_p$.

Artin conjectured that the cyclotomic extension of the field of rational numbers is C_1. We see now that (6.25) is the p-adic analogue of this conjecture. (We have only shown that K, not K_∞, is C_1. Actually the same proof shows that K_∞ is C_1 provided one uses the fact that theorem (4.7) holds for the ring R_∞. Namely, Hensel's Lemma is valid for R_∞, since any finite system of polynomials over R_∞ has all its coefficients in some $W(k_m)$. And Hensel's Lemma is all that is needed to prove (4.7) - see [Gb]. R_∞ is an example of a <u>Henselian discrete valuation ring</u>, and the theorem mentioned in (5.24) holds for such rings).

CHAPTER 7

p-ADIC FIELDS

We have defined the ring $\mathbb{Z}_p$ of p-adic integers as the completion of the ring $\mathbb{Z}$ of ordinary integers under the p-adic valuation v (given by $v(a) = n$ if p^n is the highest power of the prime p dividing the integer a), and we have defined the field $\mathbb{Q}_p$ of p-adic numbers to be the field of fractions of $\mathbb{Z}_p$ (4.3). In this chapter we will investigate forms in many variables with coefficients in $\mathbb{Z}_p$. Artin conjectured that $\mathbb{Q}_p$ is C_2 (for all p). This turned out to be false, but before we consider some counterexamples, we will follow the historical path, giving the positive results (of considerable interest in themselves) which led people to believe the conjecture.

(7.1) DEFINITION. _Let the positive integers_ d _and_ i _be given. Let_ K _be a field. Suppose that any form, with co-_

<u>efficients in</u> K, <u>of degree</u> d <u>in more than</u> d^i <u>variables has a non-trivial zero in</u> K. <u>Then</u> K <u>is said to have the property</u> $C_i(d)$.

Thus K is C_i if it has the property $C_i(d)$ <u>for all</u> d.

(7.2) THEOREM. $\mathbb{Q}_p$ <u>has the property</u> $C_2(2)$ (<u>for all</u> p).

(7.3) THEOREM. $\mathbb{Q}_p$ <u>has the property</u> $C_2(3)$ (<u>for all</u> p).

When the counter-examples were discovered, they yielded the next theorem.

(7.4) THEOREM. <u>Given a prime</u> p, <u>there exist degrees</u> d <u>such that</u> $\mathbb{Q}_p$ <u>does not have the property</u> $C_2(d)$.

It is still possible that $\mathbb{Q}_p$ is C_3 for all p, since the counter-examples thus for discovered all have less than d^3 variables. On the positive side we also have the following result due to Ax and Kochen [AK].

(7.5) THEOREM. <u>Given a degree</u> d, <u>let</u> F(d) <u>be the set of primes</u> p <u>such that</u> $\mathbb{Q}_p$ <u>does not have the property</u> $C_2(d)$. <u>Then</u> F(d) <u>is a finite set.</u>

The proof of this theorem given by Ax and Kochen is indirect, and given a specific d, it is not known which primes are in the set $F(d)$. Birch and Lewis [BL 1, BL 2] had previously proved the special case $d = 5$ of the Ax-Kochen theorem. They also showed that for any $p \in F(5)$, there exists a finite extension of $\mathbb{Q}_p$ which has the property $C_2(5)$. The analogous result for $F(d)$ is not known for $d \neq 2$, 3 or 5. (In fact, it is not even known whether $F(5)$ is empty.) We will discuss the Ax-Kochen theorem further in Chapter 9.

Theorem (7.2) is due to Hasse, who gave a classification of quadratic forms over p-adic fields. For the proof we will follow [BS].

<u>Proof.</u> Any quadratic form $f(X)$ can be written

$$f(X) = \sum_{\substack{i,j=1 \\ i \leq j}}^{n} b_{ij} X_i X_j$$

where the coefficients b_{ij} are in a field K. We will assume K has characteristic $\neq 2$ (condition satisfied by the p-adic fields). This enables us to write the form as

$$f(X) = \sum_{i,j=1}^{n} a_{ij} X_i X_j$$

where $A = (a_{ij})$ is a symmetric matrix (set $a_{ij} = a_{ji} = \frac{1}{2} b_{ij}$ for $i < j$). If X denotes the column vector of the variables $X_1, \ldots, X_n$, then the form can be written in matrix notation as

$$f(X) = X'AX$$

where ' means "transpose". If we make a linear change of variables

$$X = CY$$

where C is a non-singular $n \times n$ matrix over K and Y is the column vector of new variables $Y_1, \ldots, Y_n$, then we get a quadratic form $f_C(Y)$ in the new variables whose symmetric matrix is $C'AC$. This form is said to be <u>equivalent</u> to f (or its matrix is said to be <u>equivalent</u> to A). It is then a theorem in elementary linear algebra [BS] that every quadratic form is equivalent to a diagonal form

$$f(X) = a_1X_1^2 + a_2X_2^2 + \ldots + a_nX_n^2$$

Thus the problem of the existence of a non-trivial zero of all quadratic forms in a given number of variables is reduced to the case of diagonal quadratic forms.

Now let K be the field $\underline{\underline{Q}}_p$ of p-adic numbers. We can assume the coefficients of the diagonal form f to be p-adic integers all different from zero. Moreover, we can assume the coefficients a_i are divisible by at most the first power of p, since substituions of the type $p^h X_i = Y_i$ bring us into that situation. We can then write

$$f = f_0 + pf_1$$

where

$$f_0(X) = \epsilon_1 X_1^2 + \dots + \epsilon_r X_r^2$$

$$f_1(X) = \epsilon_{r+1} X_{r+1}^2 + \dots + \epsilon_n X_n^2$$

the ϵ_i all being p-adic units (the variables having been renumbered).

Finally, we can assume that the integer r above satisfies $r \geq n - r$. Namely, the form pf is equivalent to $f_1 + pf_0$, so we could work with pf instead of f (they have the same zeros).

After these normalizations, we will consider two cases.

Case I. p is odd.

Lemma 1. If $r \geq 3$ then f_0 has a non-trivial zero in $\underline{\underline{Z}}_p$.

Proof. By Chevalley's Theorem (2.3), there is a primitive r-component vector x in $\underline{\underline{Z}}_p$ such that

$$f_0(x) \equiv 0 \quad (\text{mod } p)$$

If x_i is not divisible by p, then

$$\frac{\partial f_0}{\partial X_i}(x) = 2\varepsilon_i x_i \not\equiv 0 \pmod{p}$$

since p is odd. By Hensel's Lemma (5.23), f has a zero y in $\underline{\underline{Z}}_p$ which is congruent to x mod p. ⌟

If now $n \geq 5$, then by our normalization $r \geq 3$, hence $(y_1,\ldots,y_r, 0,\ldots, 0)$ is a non-trivial zero of f.

Case II. $p = 2$

Lemma 2. Let x be a primitive zero of f mod 8 such that for some $i \leq r$, x_i is not divisible by 2. Then f has a zero in $\underline{\underline{Z}}_2$ which is congruent to x mod 4.

Proof. We have

$$\frac{\partial f}{\partial X_i}(x) = 2\varepsilon_i x_i \not\equiv 0 \pmod{4}$$

Applying Hensel's Lemma (5.23) with $\delta = 1$ and $\pi = 2$ gives the result. ⌟

Assume now $n \geq 5$. There are two subcases to consider.

Subcase 1. $r < n$. Consider the "partial form" $g(X) = \varepsilon_1 X_1^2 + \varepsilon_2 X_2^2 + \varepsilon_3 X_3^2 + 2\varepsilon_n X_n^2$. Clearly a non-trivial zero of this form will yield a non-trivial zero of f by setting all the other variables equal to zero.

Since $\varepsilon_1 + \varepsilon_2 = 2\alpha$, $\alpha \in \underline{\underline{Z}}_2$, we have

$$\varepsilon_1 + \varepsilon_2 + 2\varepsilon_n \alpha^2 \equiv 2\alpha + 2\alpha^2 \pmod{4}$$

$$2\alpha + 2\alpha^2 = 2\alpha(1 + \alpha) \equiv 0 \pmod 4$$

so that

$$\epsilon_1 + \epsilon_2 + 2\epsilon_n\alpha^2 = 4\beta$$

with $\beta \in \underline{\underline{Z}}_2$. If we then take $x_1 = x_2 = 1$, $x_3 = 2\beta$, $x_n = \alpha$, we get

$$\begin{aligned} g(x) &= \epsilon_1 + \epsilon_2 + \epsilon_3(2\beta)^2 + 2\epsilon_n\alpha^2 \\ &= 4\beta + \epsilon_3 4\beta^2 \\ &\equiv 4\beta + 4\beta^2 \pmod 8 \\ &\equiv 0 \pmod 8 \end{aligned}$$

By Lemma 2, x can be refined to a zero of g.

<u>Subcase 2.</u> $r = n$. Then consider the "partial form" $g(X) = \epsilon_1 X_1^2 + \epsilon_2 X_2^2 + \epsilon_3 X_3^2 + \epsilon_4 X_4^2 + \epsilon_5 X_5^2$. Once again we get $\epsilon_1 + \epsilon_2 = 2\alpha_{12}$, $\epsilon_3 + \epsilon_4 = 2\alpha_{34}$. If neither α_{12} nor α_{34} is divisible by 2, we take $x_1 = x_2 = x_3 = x_4 = 1$, while if, say, $\alpha_{12} \equiv 0 \pmod 2$, set $x_1 = x_2 = 1$, $x_3 = x_4 = 0$. In either case we get

$$\epsilon_1 x_1^2 + \epsilon_2 x_2^2 + \epsilon_3 x_3^2 + \epsilon_4 x_4^2 = 4\gamma$$

with $\gamma \in \underline{\underline{Z}}_2$. Then setting $x_5 = 2\gamma$, we get

$$g(x) \equiv 4\gamma + 4\gamma^2 \equiv 0 \pmod 8$$

so that we can again apply lemma 2. ┘

We have thus proved that over $\underline{\underline{Q}}_p$, a quadratic form in five or more variables has a non-trivial zero (7.2). ┘

We next consider the theorem on cubic forms (7.3). This was proved for $p \neq 3$ by Demyanov [De] and for all p by Lewis [Lw 1]. The proof we will present is based on that of Davenport [Da 1].

We begin with a digression into multilinear algebra.

Let R be a principal ideal domain, so that for any finite family of elements of R we can speak of the greatest common divisor of the family. Let E,F be free R-modules of finite rank, and let $T: E \to F$ be a linear transformation. If (t_{ij}) is the matrix of T with respect to some bases of E and F, denote by $\delta(T)$ the greatest common divisor of the entries t_{ij} in the matrix if they are not all zero, and set $\delta(T) = 0$ if $T = 0$. This does not depend on the choice of bases, for if $T \neq 0$, then $\delta = \delta(T)$ is characterized (up to multiplication by units in R) by the following two properties:

(1) The submodule T(E) is divisible by δ within F, i.e., for every $x \in E$, there exists $y \in F$ such that $T(x) = \delta y$.

(2) An element $\alpha \in R$ is such that the submodule T(E)

is divisible by α within F if and only if α divides δ.

Let G be another free module of finite rank, $S: F \to G$ a linear transformation. Suppose the composite transformation ST is not zero. We then have the following result, which is an immediate consequence of (1).

(7.6) LEMMA. $\delta(ST)$ _is divisible by both_ $\delta(S)$ _and_ $\delta(T)$.

Assume now R has characteristic zero.
We will consider forms of degree d in n variables over R, with $d > 1$, $n > 1$. If f is such a form, we will assume that all coefficients of f are divisible by the integer $d!$ (a harmless assumption, since we will be looking for zeros of f in R). Under that hypothesis, there is associated to f a uniquely determined symmetric d-multilinear form f^* with coefficients in R such that

$$f(X) = f^*(X, X, \ldots, X) \tag{7.7}$$

We have already seen this when $d = 2$; in that case, the symmetric bilinear form f^* associated to the quadratic form f is given by

$$2f^*(X, Y) = f(X + Y) - f(X) - f(Y)$$

To work out the general case, when there are d vectors of

variables $V_1, \ldots, V_d$, one considers all systems of indices $i_1 < i_2 < \ldots < i_k$, with $1 \le k \le d$, one substitutes $X = V_{i_1} + V_{i_2} + \ldots + V_{i_k}$ into (7.7), and one expands the right side using the fact that it is symmetric and multilinear. The final formula is

$$(7.8) \qquad d!f^*(V_1, \ldots, V_d) = \sum_{\epsilon \in \{0,1\}^d} \operatorname{sgn}\epsilon \, f(\epsilon_1 V_1 + \ldots + \epsilon_d V_d)$$

where $\epsilon = (\epsilon_1, \ldots, \epsilon_d)$ consists of zeros and ones, and the sign of ϵ is plus when the number of ones is congruent to d mod 2, minus otherwise. As an example when $d = 3$, if

$$f(X) = X_1^3 + 3X_1^2X_2 + 6X_1X_2X_3$$

then

$$f^*(X, Y, Z) = X_1Y_1Z_1 + (X_1Y_1Z_2 + X_1Z_1Y_2 + Y_1Z_1X_2)$$
$$+ (X_1Y_2Z_3 + X_1Y_3Z_2 + X_2Y_1Z_3 + X_2Y_3Z_1 + X_3Y_1Z_2 + X_3Y_2Z_1)$$

This construction is sometimes called "polarization".

(7.9) DEFINITION. <u>The form</u> f <u>is called non-degenerate if for any non-singular linear change of variables</u> $Y = TX$, <u>all the variables</u> $X_1, \ldots, X_n$ <u>actually appear in the form</u> $f(TX)$.

For example, the form $(Y_1 + Y_2)^d$ is degenerate, since after the change of variables $Y_1 + Y_2 = X_1$, $Y_2 = X_2$, the variable X_2 does not appear.

(7.10) PROPOSITION. _A necessary and sufficient condition that_ f _be non-degenerate is that after any non-zero substitution_ $V_1 = x$, $x \in R^n$, _the form_ $f^*(x, V_2, \ldots, V_d)$ _of degree_ $d - 1$ _in the remaining variables be non-zero._

Proof. Suppose f is degenerate, so that X_n, say, does not appear in $g(X) = f(TX)$. Then by (7.8) the variable V_{1n} does not appear in

$$g^*(V_1, \ldots, V_d) = f^*(TV_1, \ldots, TV_d)$$

Hence, if $x \in R^n$ is any vector such that $x_1 = \ldots = x_{n-1} = 0$, $x_n \neq 0$, we have (identically)

$$g^*(x, V_2, \ldots, V_d) = g^*(0, V_2, \ldots, V_d) = 0$$

Since T is non-singular, $Tx \neq 0$, and we have

$$f^*(Tx, V_2, \ldots, V_d) = g^*(x, T^{-1}V_2, \ldots, T^{-1}V_d) = 0$$

identically.

Conversely, suppose there exist non-zero $x \in R^n$ such that

$$f^*(x, V_2, \ldots, V_d) = 0$$

The set of all $x \in R^n$ satisfying this equation is a submodule M of rank $m > 0$ (since f^* is linear in the first variable). M is a "pure" submodule of R^n (in the sense that if $\alpha y \in M$, with $\alpha \neq 0$, then $y \in M$). It then follows from the theory of modules over a principal ideal domain [Bb 2] that there is a basis $\{e_1,\ldots, e_n\}$ of R^n such that $\{e_1,\ldots, e_m\}$ is a basis of M. Let T be the automorphism of R^n taking the usual basis of R^n into this basis. Then for any $x = (x_1,\ldots, x_n) \in R^n$, we have

$$f^*(Tx, TV_2,\ldots, TV_d) = f^*(x_1e_1 + \ldots + x_ne_n, TV_2,\ldots, TV_d)$$

and this form vanishes whenever $Tx \in M$, i.e., whenever $x_{m+1} = \ldots = x_n = 0$. It follows that when we express $f^*(TX, TV_2,\ldots, TV_d)$ as a linear form in X, e.g.

$$f^*(TX, TV_2,\ldots, TV_d) = \sum_{i=1}^{n} X_i g_i(V_2,\ldots,V_d)$$

where each g_i is (d-1)-multilinear, the forms $g_1,\ldots, g_m$ must be identically zero, so that the variables $X_1,\ldots, X_m$ do not appear. By symmetry, the variables $V_{j1},\ldots, V_{jm}$ do not appear either, for all $j = 2,\ldots, n$. Hence the variables $X_1,\ldots, X_m$ do not appear in $f(TX) = f^*(TX, TX,\ldots, TX)$. ⌟

Let us denote by $S = S_{n,d-1}$ the free module of symmetric (d-1)-multilinear forms in variables $(V_2,\ldots, V_d)$, where each V_i is a vector of n variables. For each $x \in R^n$, we have $f^*(x, V_2,\ldots, V_d) \in S$. Define a linear transformation f_1 from R^n to S by

$$f_1(x) = f^*(x, V_2,\ldots, V_d)$$

Then (7.10) says that f is non-degenerate if and only if the transformation f_1 is <u>injective</u>. Since rank S ≥ n, it is equivalent to say that f_1 has maximal rank n. In matrix terms, this means that some minor of order n in a matrix representing f_1 is non-zero. This condition can also be stated in terms of exterior powers [Bb 1]. Namely, $\overset{n}{\Lambda}R^n$ is a free module of rank 1. Then f_1 is injective if and only if the induced tranformation

$$\overset{n}{\Lambda}f_1 : \overset{n}{\Lambda}R^n \to \overset{n}{\Lambda}S$$

is non-zero (the components of a vector representing this transformation are all the minors of order n of a matrix representing f_1). We define an invariant h(f) of the form f by

$$h(f) = \delta(\overset{n}{\Lambda}f_1)$$

<u>Thus</u> h(f) = 0 <u>if and only if</u> f <u>is degenerate;</u> when f is

non-degenerate, $h(f)$ is the greatest common divisor of the minors of order n of a matrix representing f_1). For example, when f is a quadratic form, $h(f)$ is just the discriminant of f (determinant of the matrix of coefficients of the bilinear form f^*).

Consider now a non-singular linear change of variables $Y = TX$ and the transform f_T of f under this change, given by

$$f_T(X) = f(TX)$$

(7.11) PROPOSITION. $h(f_T)$ *is divisible by* $h(f)\det T$, *where* $\det T$ *is the determinant of* T.

Proof. T induces a non-singular linear transformation T^* of S into itself given by

$$g(V_2,\ldots, V_d) \to g(TV_2,\ldots, TV_d)$$

The linear transformation $(f_T)_1\colon R^n \to S$ associated to f_T is just the composite

$$R^n \xrightarrow{T} R^n \xrightarrow{f_1} S \xrightarrow{T^*} S$$

Hence $\overset{n}{\Lambda}(f_T)_1$ is just the composite

$$\overset{n}{\Lambda}R^n \xrightarrow{\overset{n}{\Lambda}T} \overset{n}{\Lambda}R^n \xrightarrow{\overset{n}{\Lambda}f_1} \overset{n}{\Lambda}S \xrightarrow{\overset{n}{\Lambda}T^*} \overset{n}{\Lambda}S$$

Now the transformation $\overset{n}{\Lambda}T$ is just multiplication by the scalar det T, hence

$$\delta(\overset{n}{\Lambda}f_1T) = \delta(\overset{n}{\Lambda}f_1)\det T = h(f)\det T$$

The proposition then follows from (7.6) applied to the composite of $\overset{n}{\Lambda}f_1T$ with $\overset{n}{\Lambda}T^*$. ⌟

(7.12) COROLLARY. _If_ T _is an automorphism of_ R^n, _then_ $h(f_T) = h(f)$.

Proof. The hypothesis on T means that det T is a unit in R, hence we can apply the proposition to f_T instead of f and T^{-1} instead of T. ⌟

Thus h(f) is an invariant of the equivalence class of f over R.

Note. The reader who is unfamiliar with exterior algebra will find a more down-to-earth treatment of the invariant h(f) in [Da], where the exterior algebra is replaced by a calculation with determinants.

We return now to cubic forms and to the proof of (7.3). We can no longer diagonalize the form f, but we can make non-singular linear changes of variables which will get us into a situation where we can apply Hensel's Lemma. The invariant $h(f)$ will be used at the last stage to show that the process converges.

Let f be any form with coefficients in the ring of p-adic integers. We will say that f is Henselian mod p^λ if there is a solution x to the congruence

$$f(x) \equiv 0 \pmod{p^{2\lambda-1}}$$

satisfying

$$\frac{\partial f}{\partial X_i}(x) \not\equiv 0 \pmod{p^\lambda} \quad \text{for some } i.$$

In that case the hypothesis of Hensel's Lemma is satisfied with $\lambda = \delta + 1$ (5.23), so that f has a p-adic zero y such that

$$y \equiv x \pmod{p^\lambda}$$

In particular, f is also Henselian mod $p^{\lambda+\nu}$ for all $\nu \geq 0$.

We assume until further notice that f has degree 3 in n variables over $\mathbb{Z}_p$.

Lemma 3. If $n \geq 4$ and f is not Henselian mod p, then f <u>is equivalent to a form of the type</u>

$$f'(X_1,X_2,X_3) + pf''(X_1,\ldots,X_n)$$

(<u>where</u> f', f" <u>are other cubic forms</u>).

<u>Proof.</u> Since $n \geq 4$, f has a primitive zero x mod p (Chevally's theorem 2.3). Since f is not Henselian mod p, all the partial derivatives at x vanish mod p. After applying a suitable automorphism of R^n, we can take $x = (1, 0,\ldots, 0)$. We set

$$f(X) = apX_1^3 + pX_1^2(b_2X_2 +\ldots+ b_nX_n)$$
$$+ X_1q(X_2,\ldots, X_n) + f_{n-1}(X_2,\ldots, X_n)$$

where q is quadratic and f_{n-1} is cubic; here the coefficients of $X_1^2X_j$, $j \neq 1$, are all divisible by p because they are the values of the partial derivatives

$\frac{\partial f}{\partial X_j}$, $j \neq 1$, at $(1, 0,\ldots, 0)$, and the coefficient of X_1^3 must be divisible by p in order to have

$$f(1, 0,\ldots, 0) \equiv 0 \pmod p$$

Next, we claim that the coefficients of q are all divisible by p. If not, then by taking values of the type $(1, 0,\ldots, 0)$ or $(1, 1, 0,\ldots, 0)$ we can find $y_2,\ldots, y_n$

such that

$$q(y_2,\dots, y_n) \not\equiv 0 \pmod p$$

In that case we can find y_1 such that

$$y_1 q(y_2,\dots, y_n) + f_{n-1}(y_2,\dots, y_n) \equiv 0 \pmod p$$

But then $\frac{\partial f}{\partial X_1}$ at the point $y = (y_1,\dots, y_n)$ is congruent to $q(y_2,\dots, y_n)$ mod p, so does not vanish; since y is a zero of f mod p, this contradicts our hypothesis. Thus

$$f(X) = pX_1 q_n(X_1, X_2,\dots, X_n) + f_{n-1}(X_2,\dots, X_n)$$

where q_n is a quadratic form. When $n = 4$ we are finished (renumber the variables).

Suppose $n \geq 5$. Then we can substitute 0 for X_1 and apply the argument to $f_{n-1}(X_2,\dots, X_n)$, since this form also cannot be Henselian mod p. Thus f_{n-1} is equivalent to

$$pX_2 q_{n-1}(X_2,\dots, X_n) + f_{n-2}(X_3,\dots, X_n)$$

The process continues until we reach $f_3(X_{n-2}, X_{n-1}, X_n)$, where Chevalley's theorem no longer applies. Hence f is equivalent to a form of the type

$$p(X_1 q_n +\dots+ X_{n-3} q_4) + f_3(X_{n-2}, X_{n-1}, X_n)$$

Reversing the order of writing the variables gives the result of lemma 3. ⌟

Lemma 4. *Hypotheses and notation being the same as in the previous lemma, suppose that the form* $f''(0, 0, 0, X_4, \ldots, X_n)$ *is Henselian mod* p^{λ}. *Then* f *is Henselian mod* $p^{\lambda+1}$.

Proof. By hypothesis (and Hensel's lemma), there exist $x_4, \ldots, x_n \in R$ such that

$$f''(0, 0, 0, x_4, \ldots, x_n) = 0$$

with the partial derivatives $\frac{\partial f''}{\partial X_4}, \ldots, \frac{\partial f''}{\partial X_n}$ at $(0, 0, 0, x_4, \ldots, x_n)$ not all congruent to zero mod p^{λ}. But then

$$f(0, 0, 0, x_4, \ldots, x_n) = 0$$

with the partial derivatives $\frac{\partial f}{\partial X_1}, \ldots, \frac{\partial f}{\partial X_n}$ at $(0, 0, 0, x_4, \ldots, x_n)$ not all congruent to zero mod $p^{\lambda+1}$. ⌟

Lemma 5. *If* $n \geq 10$ *and* f *is not Henselian mod* p^3, *then* f *is equivalent to a form of the type*

$$g(X_1, \ldots, X_q, pX_{10}, \ldots, pX_n)$$

Proof. We may assume by lemma 3 that if

$$f(X) = f'(X_1, X_2, X_3) + pf''(X_1,\ldots, X_n)$$

Putting $X_1 = pY_1$, $X_2 = pY_2$, $X_3 = pY_3$, we get

$$f(pY_1, pY_2, pY_3, X_4,\ldots, X_n) = p_3f'(Y_1, Y_2, Y_3) +$$
$$pf''(pY_1, pY_2, pY_3, X_4,\ldots, X_n)$$

Reading this equation mod p^3, we get

$$(1) \quad f(pY_1, pY_2, pY_3, X_4,\ldots, X_n) \equiv p^2f_{1,2}(Y_1, Y_2, Y_3 | X_4,\ldots,X_n)$$
$$+ pf''(0, 0, 0, X_4,\ldots, X_n)$$

where $f_{1,2}$ denotes a form which is linear in Y_1, Y_2, Y_3 and quadratic in $X_4,\ldots, X_n$. By the hypothesis and the previous lemma, $f''(0, 0, 0, X_4,\ldots, X_n)$ is not Henselian mod p^2 (a fortiori, mod p). Apply Lemma 3 to this form and substitute $X_4 = pY_4$, $X_5 = pY_5$, $X_6 = pY_6$; reading the result mod p^2 gives

$$(2) \quad f''(0, 0, 0, pY_4, pY_5, pY_6, X_7,\ldots, X_n) \equiv$$
$$pf^{(3)}(0,\ldots, 0, X_7,\ldots, X_n) \qquad (\text{mod } p^2)$$

Using the previous lemma again, the form $f^{(3)}(0,\ldots, 0, X_7,\ldots, X_n)$ is not Henselian mod p. Substituting (2) into (1), we obtain a congruence mod p^3 of the type

$$(3)\quad f(pY_1,\ldots, pY_6, X_7,\ldots, X_n) \equiv p^2(Y_1q_1 + Y_2q_2 + Y_3q_3) + p^2f^{(3)}(0,\ldots, 0, X_7,\ldots, X_n)$$

where q_1, q_2, q_3 are quadratic forms in $X_7,\ldots, X_n$. Notice that Y_4, Y_5, Y_6 do not appear on the right side.

We claim that q_1, q_2 and q_3 are all identically zero mod p. For suppose $q_1 \not\equiv 0 \pmod p$. In that case there exist $x_7,\ldots, x_n$ such that $q_1(x_7,\ldots, x_n) \not\equiv 0 \pmod p$. We can find y_1, y_2, y_3 such that

$$y_1q_1(x) + y_2q_2(x) + y_3q_3(x) + f^{(3)}(0,\ldots, 0, x_7,\ldots, x_n) \equiv 0 \pmod p$$

so that

$$f(py_1,\ldots, py_6, x_7,\ldots, x_n) \equiv 0 \pmod{p^3}$$

for <u>all</u> y_4, y_5, y_6. Let $x_i = py_i$ for $i = 1,\ldots, 6$. Then

$$\frac{\partial f}{\partial X_1}(x_1,\ldots, x_n) \equiv pq_1(x_7,\ldots, x_n) \not\equiv 0 \pmod{p^2}$$

Thus f is Henselian mod p^2, contradicting the hypothesis. Hence (3) simplifies to

$$(4)\quad f(pY_1,\ldots, pY_6, X_7,\ldots, X_n) \equiv p^2f^{(3)}(0,\ldots, 0, X_7,\ldots, X_n) \pmod{p^3}$$

We now apply Lemma 3 one last time to the form $f^{(3)}(0, \ldots, 0, X_7, \ldots, X_n)$ which (as already noted) is not Henselian mod p. We get

$$f^{(3)}(0, \ldots, 0, X_7, \ldots, X_n) \equiv f^{(4)}(X_7, X_8, X_9) \pmod{p}$$

and once more setting $X_7 = pY_7$, $X_8 = pY_8$, $X_9 = pY_9$ and substituting in (4), we find

$$f(pY_1, \ldots, pY_9, X_{10}, \ldots, X_n) \equiv 0 \pmod{p^3}$$

Write this form in $Y_1, \ldots, Y_9, X_{10}, \ldots, X_n$ as $p^3 g(Y_1, \ldots, Y_9, X_{10}, \ldots, X_n)$. Then since g is homogeneous of degree 3 we obtain

$$f(X_1, \ldots, X_n) = g(X_1, \ldots, X_q, pX_{10}, \ldots, pX_n)$$

(In this proof, we have taken the liberty of writing equality instead of equivalence every time Lemma 3 was applied). ⌟

Lemma 6. With the same hypotheses and notation as in the previous lemma, if the form $g(X_1, \ldots, X_n)$ is Henselian mod p^λ then f is Henselian mod $p^{\lambda+3}$.

Proof. By Hensel's Lemma, there exist $y_1, \ldots, y_n$ such that

$$g(y_1, \ldots, y_n) = 0$$

with some partial derivative $\frac{\partial g}{\partial Y_i}$ at (y) not congruent to zero mod p^λ. Since

$$f(pY_1, \ldots, pY_9, Y_{10}, \ldots, Y_n) = p^3 g(Y_1, \ldots, Y_n)$$

we have $f(x) = 0$, with $x_i = py_i$ for $1 \le i \le 9$ and $x_i = y_i$ for $i \ge 10$, and some partial derivative $\frac{\partial f}{\partial X_i}$ at (x) is not congruent to zero mod $p^{\lambda+3}$. ⌟

We now prove Theorem (7.3): Let f be a cubic form over $\underline{\underline{Z}}_p$ in n variables, $n \ge 10$. We may assume f non-degenerate, otherwise the theorem is obvious. Under that assumption, we will show that f must be Henselian mod p^λ for some λ.

Suppose m is a positive integer such that f is not Henselian mod p^{3m}. By Lemma 5, we may assume that

$$f(X) = g(X_1, \ldots, X_9, pX_{10}, \ldots, pX_n)$$

Let T be the linear transformation given by

$$TX = (X_1, \ldots, X_9, pX_{10}, \ldots, pX_n)$$

so that $\det T = p^{n-9}$ and $f = g_T$. By Lemma 6, the form g is not Henselian mod $p^{3(m-1)}$. If $m - 1 > 0$, we can repeat the argument. Applying (7.11), we see eventually that $h(f)$ is divisible by $p^{(n-q)m}$. This places an upper bound on m. ⌟

(7.13) Note. An examination of the proofs of (7.2) and (7.3) shows that we have actually obtained the following stronger result: Let f have degree d in n variables over $\mathbb{Z}_p$, with $n > d^2$ and d = 2 or 3. *If f is non-degenerate, then a positive integer λ can be constructively determined such that f is Henselian mod p^λ. In particular, f has a non-trivial zero in $\mathbb{Z}_p$ which is non-singular (i.e., such that some partial derivative doesn't vanish).*

(7.14) Note. The next piece of evidence for Artin's conjecture was the following result of Demyanov: *Let f_1, f_2 be quadratic forms over $\mathbb{Z}_p$ in at least 9 (greater than $2^2 + 2^2$) variables. Then f_1 and f_2 have a common non-trivial zero in $\mathbb{Z}_p$* (cf. (3.4)).

An elegant proof of this result was given by Birch, Lewis and Murphy [BLM]. Their idea is similar to the one used above. Namely, they associate to the pair (f_1, f_2) an invariant $\mathscr{I}(f_1, f_2)$ defined as follows: Let F_1, F_2 be the symmetric matrices associated to the forms f_1, f_2. Let P(t) be the polynomial in t defined by

$$P(t) = \det (F_1 - tF_2)$$

Then $\mathscr{I}(f_1, f_2)$ is defined to be the discriminant of the the polynomial P(t). They then establish the transformation formula

$$\mathcal{J}(a_{11}f_{1T} + a_{12}f_{2T}, a_{21}f_{1T} + a_{22}f_{2T}) =$$
$$(\det A)^{n(n-1)}(\det T)^{4(n-1)}\mathcal{J}(f_1, f_2)$$

where T is a linear transformation and A is the matrix (a_{ij}).

They then consider, for each non-singular T, the "pencil" of all forms $\alpha_1 f_{1T} - \alpha_2 f_{2T}$, for all α_1, α_2. When $\mathcal{J}(f_1, f_2) \neq 0$, then one can assume (v being the p-adic valuation) that

$$v(\mathcal{J}(f_1, f_2)) = \min v(\mathcal{J}(f_1', f_2'))$$

where (f_1', f_2') runs through all pairs of forms which can generate one of the pencils. Under this assumption, it follows from manipulating the transformation formula above that Hensel's Lemma (5.21) can be applied to the pair (f_1, f_2). This is the analogue of the non-degenerate case of (7.3). In the case $\mathcal{J}(f_1, f_2) = 0$, they then show that (f_1, f_2) is the p-adic limit of a sequence of pairs having non-zero invariants. For the details, see [BLM].

They have also proved the theorem for three quadratic forms in 13 variables (unpublished - too messy).

(7.15) <u>Note.</u> Theorems (7.2), (7.3) and (7.14) are valid more generally when $\underline{\underline{Z}}_p$ is replaced by any complete discrete valuation ring R whose residue field is finite (exercise).

For many years, there were attempts made to extend the previous results to degree 4. Some difficulties began to appear in print [Lw 2]. Then in 1966, Terjanian [Te] found a counter-example. He discovered a quartic form $f(X_1, X_2, X_3)$ over $\underline{\underline{Z}}_2$ in 3 variables with the property that for every primitive vector $x = (x_1, x_2, x_3)$ in $\underline{\underline{Z}}_2$,

$$f(x) \equiv 1 \pmod 4$$

Using this form, let Y, Z be other independent vectors of 3 variables each, and consider the form

$$g(X, Y, Z) = f(X) + f(Y) + f(Z)$$

Then for any primitive vector (x, y, z) in $(\underline{\underline{Z}}_2)^9$, we have

$$g(x, y, z) \equiv 1, 2 \text{ or } 3 \pmod 4$$

We can then use the same trick as in the proof of (4.10): Let U, V, W be other independent vectors of 3 variables each, and consider the quartic form

$$h(X, Y, Z, U, V, W) = g(X, Y, Z) + 4g(U, V, W)$$

in 18 variables. We claim h has no primitive zero mod 16. For suppose

$$h(x, y, z, u, v, w) \equiv 0 \pmod{16}$$

Then in particular

$$g(x, y, z) \equiv 0 \pmod{4}$$

so that (x, y, z) is not primitive. Let $(x, y, z) \equiv 2(x', y', z')$, so that

$$g(x, y, z) = 16g(x', y', z')$$

Substituting this in the congruence for h and dividing by 4 gives

$$g(u, v, w) \equiv 0 \pmod{4}$$

Hence (u, v, w) is not primitive either.

The key to this construction is the form f, which is given explicitly by

$$f(X_1, X_2, X_3) = \sum X_i^4 - \sum X_i^2 X_j^2 - \sum X_i^2 X_j X_k$$

Then $f(1, 0, 0) = f(1, 1, 0) = 1$, and

$$f(1, 1, 1) = -3 \equiv 1 \pmod{4}$$

Next compute the partial derivatives of f mod 2. For example

$$\frac{\partial f}{\partial X_1} \equiv -X_2^2X_3 - X_2X_3^2 \quad (\text{mod } 2)$$

Now for any $\alpha \in \underline{\underline{Z}}_2$, $\alpha \equiv \alpha^2 \pmod 2$, so for any $x = (x_1, x_2, x_3)$, we have

$$\frac{\partial f}{\partial X_1}(x) \equiv -2x_2x_3 \equiv 0 \quad (\text{mod } 2)$$

Since f is symmetric, we also have

$$\frac{\partial f}{\partial X_2}(x) \equiv \frac{\partial f}{\partial X_3}(x) \equiv 0 \quad (\text{mod } 2)$$

Finally if $x = (x_1, x_2, x_3)$ is primitive, then express x_i as

$$x_i \equiv \epsilon_i + 2x_i' \quad (\text{mod } 4) \qquad \epsilon_i = 0 \text{ or } 1$$

and compute f(x) mod 4 by the Taylor expansion to get

$$f(x) \equiv 1 \quad (\text{mod } 4)$$

For example,

$$f(1, 2, 3) \equiv f(1, 0, 1) + 2\sum_{i=1}^{3} \frac{\partial f}{\partial X_i}(0, 2, 2) \quad (\text{mod } 4)$$

$$\equiv 1 \quad (\text{mod } 4)$$

by the symmetry of f.

Thus $\underline{\underline{Q}}_2$ does not have the property $C_2(4)$. ⌟

Note. Consider the field $\mathbb{F}_4$ with 4 elements

$$\mathbb{F}_4 = \{0, 1, \xi, \xi^2\} \quad \xi^3 = 1$$

obtained from $\mathbb{Z}/2$ by adjoining a primitive cube root ξ of 1; the minimal equation of ξ is

$$\xi^2 + \xi + 1 = 0$$

Let $R = W(\mathbb{F}_4)$ be the complete discrete unramified valuation ring of characteristic zero having residue field $\mathbb{F}_4$ (6.3 and 6.22). Let $\bar{f}$ be the quartic form over $\mathbb{Z}/2$ obtained from the form f above by reduction mod 2. Then

$$\bar{f}(0, 1, \xi) = (1^4 + \xi^4) + 1^2\xi^2$$

$$= 1 + \xi + \xi^2 = 0$$

and

$$\frac{\partial\bar{f}}{\partial X_1}(0, 1, \xi) = 1^2\xi + 1\xi^2$$

$$= \xi + \xi^2 = 1$$

Thus $(0, 1, \xi)$ in a non-singular zero of $\bar{f}$ in $\mathbb{F}_4$, so that by Hensel's Lemma, f has a primitive zero in R. A fortiori, the form h above has a primitive zero in R. Thus it is still possible that the field of fractions of R, which is a quadratic extension of $\mathbb{Q}_2$, may have the property $C_2(4)$.

For p an odd prime, Schanuel (unpublished) gave an example to show that $\underline{\underline{Q}}_p$ does not have the property $C_2(p(p - 1))$. He constructed a form h of degree $p(p - 1)$ in $p(p + 1)(p - 1)^2$ variables with no primitive zero. The method is similar to the example above.

Namely, Schanuel produced a form $f(X_1, X_2)$ of degree $d = p(p - 1)$ in 2 variables over $\underline{\underline{Z}}_p$ such that if $x = (x_1, x_2)$ is primitive, then

$$f(x) \equiv 1 \pmod{p^2}$$

Hence, if g is the form of degree d in $2(p^2 - 1)$ variables given by

$$g(V) = f(V_1) + f(V_2) + \ldots + f(V_{p^2-1})$$

(each V_i being a vector of 2 variables), we have

$$g(v) \not\equiv 0 \pmod{p^2}$$

for any primitive v. Finally define h of degree d in $n = p(p + 1)(p - 1)^2$ variables by

$$h = g_0 + p^2 g_2 + p^4 g_4 + \ldots + p^{d-2} g_{d-2}$$

where $g_0, g_2, \ldots, g_{d-2}$ are copies of g with new variables in each copy. By the same argument as before, h has no primitive zero mod p^d, and since $n > d^2$ we have a counter-example. ⌟

In this case the form f is given explicitly by

$$f(X, Y) = \Phi(X^{p-1}, Y^{p-1})$$

where

$$\Phi(X, Y) = X^p + Y^p - \frac{1}{2}(X^{p-1}Y + XY^{p-1})$$

(7.16) LEMMA. <u>If one of</u> x, y <u>is congruent to</u> 1 <u>mod</u> p <u>and the other one is either congruent to</u> 1 <u>mod</u> p <u>or is congruent to</u> 0 <u>mod</u> p^2, <u>then</u>

$$\Phi(x, y) \equiv 1 \pmod{p^2}$$

<u>Proof.</u> Say $x = 1 + p\xi$. Then

$$x^{p-1} \equiv 1 - p\xi \pmod{p^2}$$

$$x^p \equiv 1 \pmod{p^2}$$

<u>Case 1.</u> $y = p^2\eta$. Then

$$y^{p-1} \equiv y^p \equiv 0 \pmod{p^2}$$

$$\Phi(x, y) \equiv x^p \equiv 1 \pmod{p^2}$$

Case 2. $y = 1 + p\eta$. Then

$$x^p + y^p \equiv 2 \pmod{p^2}$$

$$x^{p-1}y \equiv 1 + p(\eta - \xi) \pmod{p^2}$$

$$xy^{p-1} \equiv 1 + p(\xi - \eta) \pmod{p^2}$$

which again gives $\Phi(x, y) \equiv 2 - \frac{1}{2}(2) = 1 \pmod{p^2}$.

From this lemma we can deduce that $f(x,y) \equiv 1 \pmod{p^2}$ whenever (x,y) is primitive. Namely, if x and y are both units in $\mathbb{Z}_p$, then

$$x^{p-1} \equiv y^{p-1} \equiv 1 \pmod{p}$$

whereas if x, say, is a unit and $y = p\eta$, then

$$y^{p-1} = p^{p-1}\eta^{p-1} \equiv 0 \pmod{p^2}$$

so that in either case, the pair (x^{p-1}, y^{p-1}) satisfies the hypothesis of the lemma. ⌟

These examples of Terjanian and Schanuel furnish a proof of (7.4). ⌟

Schanuel also considers the form

$$\Phi(X_1,\ldots, X_{p-1}) = \sum X_i^p - \frac{1}{2}\sum X_i^{p-1}X_j + \frac{1}{3}\sum X_i^{p-2}X_jX_k$$
$$-\ldots - \frac{1}{p-1}\sum X_i^2X_{j_1}X_{j_2}\ldots X_{j_{p-2}}$$

and shows that it satisfies the analogue of lemma (7.16). Using the same method as before with this new Φ , he gets a counter-example of degree $p(p - 1)$ in even more variables. Moreover, by substituting Φ into itself repeatedly (cf. Chapter 3), he is able to get counter-examples of degree $p^k(p - 1)$ for all $k \geq 1$. Applying this self-substitution trick to Terjanian's form f, he also gets counter-examples of degree 2^k for all $k \geq 2$ over $\underline{\underline{Z}}_2$. In all these counter-examples, $n < d^3$, so $\underline{\underline{Q}}_p$ may be C_3.

We mention one more positive result, which is a consequence of the theorem of Brauer to be proved in the next chapter.

(7.17) THEOREM. _Given_ p _and_ d, _there exists an integer_ $i \geq 2$ _(which may depend on_ p _and_ d) _such that_ $\underline{\underline{Q}}_p$ _does have the property_ $C_i(d)$.

We have stated the result in this manner to be consistent with the previous discussion, but a more precise statement is that *there is an integer* $\Psi(p, d) \geq d^2$ *such that any form over* $\mathbb{Q}_p$ *of degree* d *in* n *variables, with* $n > \Psi(p, d)$, *has a non-trivial zero in* $\mathbb{Q}_p$. Taking $\Psi(p, d)$ to be minimal with respect to this property, and taking (p, d) such that $\mathbb{Q}_p$ is not $C_2(d)$, there is no evidence now for the belief that $\Psi(p, d)$ must equal a power d^i of d.

We conclude this chapter by verifying the above statement for the class of diagonal forms.

(7.18) PROPOSITION. *Let* R *be a complete discrete valuation ring of characteristic zero with finite residue field. For every integer* $d > 0$, *there is an integer* $\Psi(R, d)$ *such that if* $n > \Psi(R, d)$, *every diagonal equation of degree* d *in* n *variables over* R

$$a_1x_1^d + a_2x_2^d + \ldots + a_nx_n^d = 0$$

has a non-trivial zero in R.

Proof. We first need

(7.19) LEMMA. *Let* $R^{(d)}$ *consist of all the* d^{th} *powers of elements of* R. *Then* $R^{(d)}$ *is of finite index in* R (*in the sense that there is a finite set* $B \subset R$ *such that every*

$x \in R$ _can be expressed in the form_

$$x = y^d b$$

with $y \in R$ _and some_ $b \in B$).

Proof. Let U be the group of units in R, $U^{(d)} = R^{(d)} \cap U$. It suffices to thow that $U^{(d)}$ has finite index in U, for if $u_1, \ldots, u_r$ are representatives of the cosets and π is a uniformizing parameter in R, then the set B of elements

$$b_{ij} = u_i \pi^j \quad 1 \leq i \leq r, \quad 0 \leq j \leq d - 1$$

will do what we want.

Now U, being a projective limit of finite groups, is _compact_. Hence the finiteness will follow if we can show that $U^{(d)}$ is _open_ in U, for $U/U^{(d)}$ will then be compact and discrete. The openness of $U^{(d)}$ will follow from the existence of an open neighborhood V of 1 in U which is entirely contained in $U^{(d)}$.

Let $\delta = v(d)$, where v is the valuation on R. For any $u \in U$, consider the polynomial

$$f_u(X) = X^d - u$$

and let V be the open neighborhood consisting of all $u \in U$ such that

$$u \equiv 1 \pmod{\pi^{2\delta+1}}$$

For $u \in V$ we have

$$f_u(1) = 1 - u \equiv 0 \pmod{\pi^{2\delta+1}}$$

$$f_u'(1) = d \not\equiv 0 \pmod{\pi^{\delta+1}}$$

So by Hensel's Lemma (5.9) there is a unique $v \in R$ such that

$$v^d = u$$

$$v \equiv 1 \pmod{\pi^{\delta+1}}$$

┘

Returning to our diagonal form, we express each coefficient a_i as

$$a_i = \alpha_i^d b_i \qquad 1 \leq i \leq n$$

with $\alpha_i \in R$ and b_i one of the representatives of R mod $R^{(d)}$; with this system of indexing, it is possible that $b_i = b_j$ for $i \neq j$. Let N_d be the cardinality of B. We may assume all $a_i \neq 0$, otherwise there is an obvious non-trivial solution to the diagonal equation.

<u>Case 1.</u> d <u>odd</u>. Then we can take $\Psi(R,d) = N_d$. For if $n > N_d$, we have $b_i = b_j$ for some $i \neq j$, say $b_1 = b_2$. Then $(-\alpha_2, \alpha_1, 0, \ldots, 0)$ is a non-trivial solution.

Case 2. d even. Then we need another lemma.

(7.20) LEMMA. There exist negative integers which have $d^{\underline{th}}$ roots in R.

Proof. The argument is the same as before, since there exist negative integer -m which satisfy the congruence

$$-m \equiv 1 \pmod{\pi^{2\delta+1}}$$

where $\delta = v(d)$. ⌟

Let m_d be the smallest positive integer such that $-m_d$ has a $d^{\underline{th}}$ root in R, and let

$$-m_d = \mu^d$$

with $\mu \in R$. Then we can take $\Psi(R,d) = (1 + m_d)N_d$. For if $n > (1 + m_d)N_d$, some $b \in B$ occurs as b_i for at least $1 + m_d$ distinct indices i, say $i = 1,2,\ldots, m_d + 1$. Let

$$\beta_i = \prod_{\substack{j \neq i \\ 1 \leq j \leq m_d+1}} \alpha_j \qquad 1 \leq i \leq m_d + 1$$

Then $(\mu\beta_1, \beta_2, \beta_3, \ldots, \beta_{m_d+1}, 0, \ldots, 0)$ is a non-trivial solution. ⌟

(7.21) Example. Let $d = 2$, $R = \mathbb{Z}_3$. Any $u \in U^{(2)}$ must have a square root mod 3, so we must have

$$u \equiv 1 \pmod 3$$

Since in this case $\delta = 0$, this congruence is also sufficient for u to have a square root. Thus

$$[U: U^{(2)}] = 2$$

whence $N_2 = 4$. Since $m_2 = 2$ here, we get from the construction above $\Psi(\underline{\underline{Z}}_3, 2) \leq 12$. This is too crude, since we know from (7.2) that we can take $\Psi(\underline{\underline{Z}}_p, 2) = 4$.

CHAPTER 8

THE THEOREM OF BRAUER AND BIRCH

It is the following result.

(8.1) THEOREM. *Let* K *be a field.*

(*Brauer*). *Assume that for every integer* $d > 0$, *there exists an integer* $\Phi(d)$ *such that for* $n > \Phi(d)$, *every diagonal form of degree* d *in* n *variables over* K *has a non-trivial zero in* K.

Let $h \geq 1$, $m \geq 1$ *be integers, and* $d_1, \ldots, d_h$ *positive integers. Then there exists an integer* $\Psi(d_1, \ldots, d_h; m)$ *such that for*

$$n > \Psi(d_1, \ldots, d_h; m)$$

every system $\{f_1, \ldots, f_h\}$ *of* h *forms in* n *variables over* K *such that*

$$\text{degree } f_i = d_i \qquad 1 \leq i \leq h$$

has an m*-dimensional vector space of common zeros in* K.

(*Birch*). *Restrict the hypothesis above to degrees* d *which are odd. Then the conclusion subsists when restricted to degrees* $d_1, \ldots, d_h$ *that are odd.*

Before giving the proof, we will make some comments and state some corollaries.

First of all, the presence of the integer m, which may seem to make matters unnecessarily complicated, is essential for the induction used in the proof.

Secondly, let us consider some fields where these hypotheses are satisfied. *Let* R *be a complete discrete valuation ring of characteristic zero having finite residue field, and let* K *be the field of fractions of* R. Then by (7.18), K satisfies the Brauer hypothesis. We therefore get the next corollary.

(8.2) *COROLLARY. For* R *as above, given any* $d > 0$, *there exists an integer* $\Psi(R, d)$ *such that for* $n > \Psi(R, d)$, *any form of degree* d *in* n *variables over* R *has a non-trivial zero in* R. *We have*

$$\Psi(R, d) \geq d^2$$

The last inequality follows from (4.10).

Next, let K be an algebraic number field (of finite degree over the field of rational numbers). Then K satisfies the Birch hypothesis, by a difficult theorem of Peck [P]. According to Birch [B 2], the case $K = \mathbb{Q}$ of Peck's theorem "was well-known before the [second world] war, being capable of proof by a straightforward modification of the Hardy-Littlewood method for Waring's Problem". And Lewis has remarked that by taking a vector space basis of K over $\mathbb{Q}$, the conclusion of Birch's theorem for K can be deduced from the conclusion for $\mathbb{Q}$. In any case, we have the following corollary.

(8.3) COROLLARY. *Let* K *be an algebraic number field*, d *an odd positive integer. Then there is an integer* $\Psi(K, d)$ *such that for* $n > \Psi(K, d)$, *any form of degree* d *in* n *variables over* K *has a non-trivial zero in* K. *We have*

$$\Psi(K,d) \geq d^2$$

The last inequality again follows from (4.10) by passing to a completion of K with respect to a discrete valuation.

The case of cubic forms has been studied in detail by Davenport [Da 2], who has shown using analytic techniques that

$$\Psi(K, 3) \leq 15$$

It is conjectured that $\Psi(K, 3) = 9$, with the local result (7.3) providing support for the conjecture. A proof that $\Psi(\mathbb{Q}, 3) \leq 16$ will be found in Davenport's lectures [Da 1], as well as a treatment of Peck's theorem over $\mathbb{Q}$ and Waring's Problem (representing integers as sums of dth powers of integers). The methods are analytic and beyond the scope of this book.

Corollary (8.3) refers only to odd degrees d. Its statement remains valid for $d = 2$ with $\Psi(K, 2) = 4$, provided we restrict ourselves to indefinite quadratic forms (or provided K is totally imaginary). This follows from the local result (7.2) and the theorem of Hasse which classifies quadratic forms over a number field in terms of all the completions (archimedean and ultrametric) of the number field (see [BS] for an elementary treatment). Hasse's theorem implies that a quadratic form has a non-trivial zero in K if and only if it has a non-trivial zero in every completion of K. The analogous statement for cubic forms is false, as was shown by Selmer with the simple example

$$f(X, Y, Z) = 3X^3 + 4Y^3 + 5Z^3$$

([BS], p. 72) over the field of rational numbers. The search for an appropriate substitute for cubic forms for the "Hasse Principle" has attracted intense interest on the part of the best algebraic geometers and number theorists, leading to some of the most fascinating conjectures in mathematics today [Ca].

We will now prove Brauer's theorem, giving the modifications needed for Birch's result in parentheses.

We first improve on our hypothesis in (8.1).

(8.4) LEMMA. <u>Given integers</u> $m \geq 1$ <u>and</u> d (<u>odd</u>), <u>there exists an integer</u> $\Phi(d; m)$ <u>such that for</u> $n \geq \Phi(d; m)$, <u>every diagonal form of degree</u> d <u>in</u> n <u>variables over</u> K <u>has an</u> m-<u>dimensional vector space of zero in</u> K.

<u>Proof.</u> We will show that $\Phi(d; m) = m(\Phi(d) + 1)$ will do, where $\Phi(d)$ is the integer in the hypothesis (8.1). Let $r = \Phi(d) + 1$. If c_1 is the coefficient of X_i^d in the given diagonal form f, consider the equations

$$c_1X_1^d + \ldots + c_rX_r^d = 0$$

$$c_{r+1}X_{r+1}^d + \ldots + c_{2r}X_{2r}^d = 0$$

$$\vdots$$

By hypothesis, the first equation has a non-trivial zero $(a_1,\ldots, a_r)$ in K, the second equation a non-trivial zero $(a_{r+1},\ldots, a_{2r})$ in K, etc. Then for every $(x_1,\ldots, x_m) \in K^m$, the vector

$$(x_1a_1,\ldots, x_1a_r, x_2a_{r+1},\ldots, x_2a_{2r},\ldots, x_ma_{(m-1)r+1},\ldots, x_ma_{mr}, 0,\ldots, 0)$$

is a zero fo f, and these vectors fill up the required vector space. ∎

In the theorem we must deal with a system $\{f_1,\ldots, f_h\}$ of forms of degrees $d_1,\ldots, d_h$. Let

$$d = \max_{1\le i\le h} d_i$$

The theorem will be proved by double induction on d and h. The beginning of the induction $d = 1$, h arbitrary, is a standard result of linear algebra.

<u>Step 1.</u> Given $d > 1$. Assume the theorem holds for all (odd) degrees less than d and any number of forms of such degrees. We will then show that the theorem holds for one form f of degree d.

The idea of the proof of this step is to show that if n is sufficiently large, f is equivalent to a diagonal form in $\Phi(d; m)$ variables, so that Lemma (8.4) applies. Since we can split off one variable at a time, this diagonalization will be achieved by repeatedly applying the following sub-lemma.

(8.5) SUBLEMMA. *Given any* $\nu \geq 0$. *Under the hypothesis of Step* 1, *there exists an integer* $n_1(d, \nu)$ *such that if* $n \geq n_1(d, \nu)$, f *is equivalent to a form of the type*

$$c_0 Z_0^d + g_1(Z_1, \ldots, Z_\nu)$$

(*if* $\nu = 0$ then $g_1 = 0$).

Proof. For greater clarity, we will use underscoring such as $\underline{\underline{x}}$ to denote a vector. A system of vectors will be numbered by superscripts, their components by subscripts, e.g.,

$$\underline{\underline{x}}^{(i)} = (x_1^{(i)}, x_2^{(i)}, \ldots, x_n^{(i)})$$

Let $\underline{\underline{X}}^{(i)}, \ldots, \underline{\underline{X}}^{(d)}$ be d independent vectors of indeterminates. If f is given explicitly as

$$f(\underline{\underline{X}}) = \sum c_{i_1 i_2 \ldots i_d} X_{i_1} X_{i_2} \ldots X_{i_d}$$

where $1 \leq i_1 \leq \ldots \leq i_d \leq n$, we will consider the d-times multilinear form M defined by

$$M(\underline{\underline{X}}^{(1)}, \ldots, \underline{\underline{X}}^{(d)}) = \sum c_{i_1 i_2 \ldots i_d} X_{i_1}^{(1)} X_{i_2}^{(2)} \ldots X_{i_d}^{(d)}$$

(Note: The form f* used in Chapter 7 is obtained by symmetrizing M).

Let k be a positive integer to be specified later, and let S be some k-dimensional vector subspace of K^n. We claim that if n is sufficiently large compared to k, then there exists a non-zero vector $\underline{\underline{x}}^{(0)} \in K^n$ such that the equations

$$(8.6) \qquad M(\underbrace{\underline{\underline{x}}^{(0)}, \ldots, \underline{\underline{x}}^{(0)}}_{r}, \underbrace{\underline{\underline{y}}, \ldots, \underline{\underline{y}}}_{d-r}) = 0$$

hold for all vectors $\underline{\underline{y}} \in S$ and all (odd) r less than d.

Namely, choose a basis $\underline{\underline{x}}^{(1)}, \ldots, \underline{\underline{x}}^{(k)}$ for S. Since M is multilinear, the infinite system of equations (8.6) is a consequence of the finite system

$$M(\underline{\underline{x}}^{(0)}, \ldots, \underline{\underline{x}}^{(0)}, \underline{\underline{x}}^{(j_1)}, \ldots, \underline{\underline{x}}^{(j_{d-r})}) = 0$$

where $j_1, \ldots, j_{d-r}$ take on all values from 1 to k and r takes on all (odd) values less than d. Since these equations in $\underline{\underline{x}}^{(0)}$ all have (odd) degrees less than d, the inductive hypothesis implies they have a common non-trivial solution $\underline{\underline{x}}^{(0)} \in K^n$ provided that

$$n \geq n_0(d, k)$$

where $n_0(d, k)$ is some integer determined by d and k.

Consider next the problem of finding vectors $\underline{y} \in S$ which satisfy the equations

$$(8.7) \qquad M(\underbrace{\underline{\underline{x}}^{(0)},\ldots,\underline{\underline{x}}^{(0)}}_{d-r}, \underbrace{\underline{y},\ldots,\underline{y}}_{r}) = 0$$

for all (odd) positive r less than d. By inductive hypothesis again, these equations will be satisfied by all vector $\underline{y}$ lying in a $(\nu+1)$-dimensional subspace S_1 of S, provided that

$$k \geq k_0(d, \nu)$$

where $k_0(d, \nu)$ is some integer determined by d and ν. Let $n_1(d, \nu) = n_0(d, k_0(d, \nu))$, so that for $n \geq n_1(d, \nu)$, there exists a non-zero vector $\underline{\underline{x}}^{(0)}$ and a $(\nu+1)$-dimensional subspace $S_1 \subset K^n$ such that

$$(8.8) \qquad M(\underbrace{\underline{\underline{x}}^{(0)},\ldots,\underline{\underline{x}}^{(0)}}_{t}, \underbrace{\underline{y},\ldots,\underline{y}}_{d-t}) = 0$$

for all $\underline{y} \in S_1$ and all t less than d (whether even or odd).

Choose a basis $\underline{\underline{x}}^{(1)},\ldots,\underline{\underline{x}}^{(\nu)}, \underline{\underline{x}}^{(\nu+1)}$ of S_1 ; if $\underline{\underline{x}}^{(0)}$ happens to lie in S_1, choose this basis so that $\underline{\underline{x}}^{(0)}$, $\underline{\underline{x}}^{(1)},\ldots, x^{(\nu)}$ are linearly independent (e.g., $\underline{\underline{x}}^{(0)} = \underline{\underline{x}}^{(\nu+1)}$). Let $\underline{\underline{Y}}$ be the vector of $\nu + 1$ indeterminates defined by

$$\underline{\underline{Y}} = Y_1\underline{\underline{x}}^{(1)} + \ldots + Y_{\nu+1}\underline{\underline{x}}^{(\nu+1)}$$

Then (8.8) implies the identity in $\underline{\underline{Y}}$

$$M(\underbrace{\underline{\underline{x}}^{(0)},\ldots,\underline{\underline{x}}^{(0)}}_{t},\underbrace{\underline{\underline{Y}},\ldots,\underline{\underline{Y}}}_{d-t}) = 0$$

for all t less than d, which implies that

$$M(\underline{\underline{x}}^{(0)},\ldots,\underline{\underline{x}}^{(0)},\underline{\underline{x}}^{(j_1)},\ldots,\underline{\underline{x}}^{(j_{d-t})}) = 0 \tag{8.9}$$

for all t less than d and all j_i with $1 \le j_i \le \nu + 1$.

We introduce a new vector $\underline{\underline{Z}}$ of $\nu + 1$ indeterminates $Z_0, Z_1,\ldots, Z_\nu$, and make the substitution

$$\underline{\underline{X}} = Z_0\underline{\underline{x}}^{(0)} + Z_1\underline{\underline{x}}^{(1)} +\ldots+ Z_\nu\underline{\underline{x}}^{(\nu)}$$

$$g(\underline{\underline{Z}}) = f(\underline{\underline{X}})$$

Then for any t less than d, the coefficient of

$$Z_0^t Z_{j_1}\ldots Z_{j_{d-1}}$$

in $g(\underline{\underline{Z}})$, where $1 \le j_i \le \nu$, is (8.9), hence

$$g(\underline{\underline{Z}}) = c_o Z_0^d + g_1(Z_1,\ldots, Z_\nu)$$

as desired. ⌋

<u>Step 2.</u> Given $d > 1$ and $h > 1$, assume the theorem holds for fewer than h forms of maximum degree $\le d$. We will

show the theorem holds for h forms of maximum degree d.

Proof. Let f_h, say, have degree d. By Step 1, if we are given m_1, then f_h has an m_1-dimensional vector space S of zeros in K, provided $n > \Psi(d; m_1)$. Let $\underline{x}^{(1)}, \ldots, \underline{x}^{(m_1)}$ be a basis of S. Consider a new vector $\underline{Y}$ of m_1 indeterminates and make the substitution

$$\underline{X} = Y_1\underline{x}^{(1)} + \ldots + Y_{m_1}\underline{x}^{(m_1)}$$

Let

$$g_i(\underline{Y}) = f_i(\underline{X}) \qquad 1 \leq i \leq h - 1$$

By inductive hypothesis, the forms $g_1, \ldots, g_{h-1}$ have an m-dimensional vector space of common zeros, provided $m_1 > \Psi(d_1, \ldots, d_{h-1}; m)$. Thus we can set

$$\Psi(d_1, \ldots, d_{h-1}, d; m) = \Psi(d; \Psi(d_1, \ldots, d_{h-1}; m))$$

We state here another remarkable global theorem due to Birch [B 1], whose proof requires analytic techniques similar to those in [Da 1].

(8.5) THEOREM. Let $f_1, \ldots, f_h$ be forms of degree d in n variables with integer coefficients, $n > h$. Let V be the algebraic variety of common zeros of these forms, and let

s *be the dimension of the subvariety of singular points on* V. *Assume*

(i) V *has a non-singular real point and a non-singular* p*-adic point for every prime* p.

(ii) V *has dimension* $n - h$.

(iii) $n - s > h(h + 1)(d - 1)2^{d-1}$

Then there is a non-trivial common zero of these forms in the domain of integers.

In other word, for sufficiently non-singular varieties which are complete intersections, the "non-singular Hasse Principle" is valid.

CHAPTER 9

METHODS OF MATHEMATICAL LOGIC

We return now to the previously stated (but not proven) theorem of Ax-Kochen (7.5) which says that given a degree d, there exists a finite set A(d) of prime numbers such that if p is a prime _not_ in A(d), then the field $\underline{\underline{Q}}_p$ of p-adic numbers has the diophantine property we called $C_2(d)$ (see 7.1). This theorem is actually one special case of an infinite number of cases in a much more general theorem of Ax-Kochen [AK] as follows:

(9.1) THEOREM. _Let_ S_p _be the field of formal meromorphic series in one variable with coefficients in the finite field_ $\underline{\underline{Z}}/p$. _For every elementary statement_ Δ, _there exists a finite set of primes_ $A(\Delta)$ _such that for every prime_ p _not in_ $A(\Delta)$, Δ _is valid in the field_ $\underline{\underline{Q}}_p$ _of_ p-_adic numbers if and only if_

Δ *is valid in* S_p.

The reader will recognize that we have entered an entirely new area, that of Mathematical Logic, where instead of proving a result about homogeneous polynomials, one goes much further and proves results about "elementary statements". To ease the transition into this vast domain of inquiry, we present another application of (9.1) to forms in many variables, a theorem originally proved by Greenleaf [Gf] using algebro-geometric methods.

(9.2) THEOREM (Greenleaf). *Let* f *be a polynomial without constant term of degree* d *in* $n > d$ *variables and having integer coefficients. Then there exists a finite set* $A(f)$ *of primes such that for every prime* p *not in* $A(f)$, f *has a non-trivial zero in* $\mathbb{Q}_p$.

This follows from (9.1) and Chevalley's Theorem (2.3), since f has a non-trivial zero in $\mathbb{Z}/p$ - a fortiori in S_p - for all p. ⌟

The complete proof of (9.1) is beyond the scope of this book, so we restrict ourselves to some opinionated comments.

For the definition of "elementary statement", we

follow [AK]: Let K be a field with a discrete valuation v and a specific uniformizing parameter π . By an "atomic formula" over K is meant an expression of the form $v(f) = v(g)$ or $v(f) > v(g)$ or $f = 0$, where f and g are polynomials with fixed coefficients in the ring $\mathbb{Z}[\pi]$. An "elementary formula" is an expression constructed in a finite number of steps from atomic formulas by means of negation, conjunction, disjunction, implication and quantifiers ("there exists an x such that" and "for all x"). An _elementary statement_ is then an elementary formula in which every variable x in the formula is bound by a quantifier. The statement is interpreted over K by assuming that its variables range over K; if, in addition, K has characteristic $p > 0$, we interpret any integers occurring in the statement mod p. The crucial restrictions on elementary statements are that they do not speak about _sets_ of elements of K but only about individual elements of K, and that the variables range only over K. (Thus the statement "K is C_2" is _not_ elementary, because there is an implicit integer variable, the degree d; the statement "K is $C_2(d)$" _is_ elementary, because it suffices to consider forms in $d^2 + 1$ variables).

The method of proof in [AK] actually uses very little Logic, only the notion of a "non-principal ultraproduct" of the fields $\mathbb{Q}_p$ or the fields S_p. For the rest, the proof relies heavily on the theory of fields with a more general kind of valuation than the discrete valuations we have considered in these lectures, in particular on Kaplansky's results on pseudo-Cauchy sequences in such fields.

The proof may be considered "non=constructive" in that it relies heavily on Zorn's Lemma for the existence of the set $A(\Delta)$.

Thus, although (9.1) is a marvelous result, it would be very **nice** to have a more constructive proof. Such a proof has recently been outlined by Paul Cohen [Co], eleminating the need for the ingenious but perhaps misleading machinery in [AK].

In [Co], the initial idea is to reconsider the field $\mathbb{R}$ of real numbers and to find p-adic analogues for results known over $\mathbb{R}$. (The reader should recall the theorem of Ostrowski [BS] that a completion of the field $\mathbb{Q}$ of rational numbers with respect to an absolute value is isomorphic to $\mathbb{Q}_p$ for some p when the absolute value is ultrametric, or to $\mathbb{R}$ otherwise). Now Tarski [Ta] gave a recursive procedure to decide the truth or falsity of any elementary statement over $\mathbb{R}$. In [Co], this "decision procedure" is re-proved very quickly, by giving "effectively" a method of determining the roots of a real polynomial in one variable. The decision procedure is valid for any real-closed field, i.e., any ordered field satisfying the real-closure property: If $x_1 < x_2$, $f(x_1) < 0$, and $f(x_2) > 0$, where f is a polynomial, then $f(y) = 0$ for some y between x_1 and x_2.

[Co] then gives a "relative decision procedure" for any field K complete under a discrete valuation, "relative" in the sense that the validity of an elementary statement over K is reduced to the question of the validity of an elementary statement over the residue ring R_m mod π^{m+1} for some m. As in the proof of Tarski's theorem, the full strength of the completeness hypothesis is not used; here, instead of the real-closure property, the crucial property is Hensel's Lemma in one variable (5.9), and this is used once again to give an "effective" method of determining the roots in K of a polynomial in one variable over K. (Note: In [AK] and in [K] are given axioms for a p-adically closed field, and a decision procedure deduced from thos axioms; however, their methods do not yield a primitive recursive procedure).

Finally, it is shown in [Co] how an elementary question about the residue ring R_m is already determined by the residue field $k = R_0$ for all but finitely many primes. This gives another proof of Ax-Kochen's theorem (7.5), in which the possible exceptional primes are given as a primitive recursive function of the degree d. (Unfortunately, the method involves elimination of one variable at a time, hence is not exactly "practical"; perhaps the use of the General Hensel Lemma (5.21) in several variables would lead to an improvement).

Note: The theory of real closed fields yields a quick solution to Hilbert's Seventeenth Problem. Namely, Artin proved, using this theory, that a positive definite rational function over $\mathbb{R}$ must be a sum of squares (see [Lg 3], p. 278). In [K], Kochen proves an analogous theorem over the field of p-adic numbers. The analogue of positivity is *integrality*. He therefore considers the ring I of those rational functions $f(X_1, \ldots, X_n) = f(X)$ such that $f(x)$ is a p-adic integer for all $x \in (\mathbb{Q}_p)^n$ for which $f(x)$ is defined. He proves the following result:

(9.3) THEOREM. *Let* R *be the* $\mathbb{Z}_p$-*algebra generated by all elements of the form*

$$\frac{1}{2p}\left[(w^p - w + 1)^{-1} + (w^p - w - 1)^{-1}\right]$$

where $w \in \mathbb{Q}_p(X)$. *Let* R_T *be the ring of fractions of* R *with respect to the multiplicatively closed set*

$$T = \{1 + pz \mid z \in R\}$$

Then I *is the integral closure of* R_T in $\underline{\underline{Q}}_p(X)$, *i.e., consists of those elements of* $\underline{\underline{Q}}_p(X)$ *which are roots of a monic polynomial with coefficients in* R_T.

The proof uses the theory of p-adically closed fields, but is model-theoretic in nature. It would be interesting to have a purely algebraic proof (presumably one could be developed using the methods in [Co]).

Note. Returning to real-closed fields again, Lang [Lg 4] has proved the following result:

(9.4) THEOREM. *Let* K *be a function field in* s *variables over a real closed field* k. *Let* $f_1, \ldots, f_r$ *be forms over* K *of odd degrees* $d_1, \ldots, d_r$, *in* n *variables. If*

$$n > d_1^s + \ldots + d_r^s$$

then these forms have a non-trivial common zero in K.

We sketch the proof in the special case $k = \underline{\underline{R}}$: By the same techniques as in the proof of theorem (3.6) - restricted to *odd* degrees - one reduces immediately to the case s = 0, so that we can take $K = \underline{\underline{R}}$ (the case $K = \underline{\underline{C}}$ being trivial). In that case we must show that for odd degree forms, if the number r of forms is less than the number n of variables, they have a common non-trivial real zero. By throwing in some linear forms if necessary, we may assume $r = n - 1$.

The trick is to find forms $f_1^*, \ldots, f_r^*$ arbitrarily close to the given special forms $f_1, \ldots, f_r$ yet generically independent over the field $\underline{\underline{Q}}$ of rational numbers. Then by Bezout's Theorem in algebraic geometry, the generic forms have $d_1 d_2 \ldots d_r$ <u>distinct</u> complex projective zeros; since the the complex conjugate of any zero is also a zero, and $d_1 d_2 \ldots d_r$ is <u>odd</u>, the generic forms must have a real projective zero. Since real projective space is <u>compact</u>, these real zeros, as the generic forms converge to the special forms, must have a point of accumulation; by <u>continuity</u>, that point must be a real zero of the special forms. ┘

If the function field K has an ordering extending the one on k - i.e., K is a <u>real field</u> - then obviously theorem (9.4) cannot be extended to even degree forms. Lang has shown that K is a real field if and only if there is an algebraic variety V over k with K as its field of rational functions such that V has a <u>simple</u> point in k [Lg 3]. He goes on to conjecture that if K is <u>not</u> real, then (9.4) can be so extended, i.e., he conjectures that a non-real function field in s variables over a real closed field is C_s.

Note (added in proof). Greenleaf [Gf] actually proved a more general theorem than (9.2), as follows:

Let f *be a polynomial (in* n *variables) with integer coefficients. Then there is a finite set of primes* A(f) *such that if* p *is not in* A(f), *then every zero of* f *mod* p *can be refined to a* p-*adic zero of* f.

This theorem is also a consequence of the Ax-Kochen result (9.1). In [Zz 1], Birch and McCann make the Greenleaf result more explicit by proving the following result.

There exists an integer $D_n(f)$, *which can be effectively calculated, such that given a prime* p *and* $x \in \mathbb{Z}^n$ *such that the power of* p *in* f(x) *exceeds the power of* p *in* $D_n(f)$, *then* x *can be refined to a* p-*adic zero of* f.

This is basically the same result as (5.24) except for the effective calculation. The methods used in [Zz 1] are essentially the same as those in [Co], i.e., Hensel's Lemma and elimination of one variable at a time.

Another paper dealing with these questions is [Zz 2].

BIBLIOGRAPHY

[A 1] J. Ax, "A field of cohomological dimension 1 which is not C_1", Bull. A. M. S. vol. 71 (1965), p. 717.

[A 2] J. Ax, "Zeros of polynomials over finite fields", Am. J. Math. vol. 86 (1964), pp. 255-261.

[AK] J. Ax and S. Kochen, "Diophantine problems over local fields": I + II, Am. J. Math. 87 (1965), pp. 605-648; III, Ann. of Math. 83 (1966), pp. 437-456.

[B 1] B.J. Birch, "Forms in many variables", Proc. Roy. Soc. Ser. A 265 (1961/62), pp. 245-263.

[B 2] B.J. Birch, "Homogeneous forms of odd degree in a large number of variables", Mathematika 4 (1957), pp. 102-105.

[BL 1] B.J. Birch and D.J. Lewis, "p-adic forms", J. Indian Math. Soc. 23 (1959), pp. 11-32.

[BL 2] B.J Birch and D.J. Lewis, "On p-adic forms", Mich. Math. J. 9 (1962), pp. 53-57.

[BLM] B.J. Birch, D.J. Lewis and T.G. Murphy, "Simultaneous quadratic forms", Am. J. Math. 84 (1962), pp. 110-115.

[BS] Z.A. Borevich and I.R. Shafarevich, "Number Theory", Academic Press, N.Y. 1966.

[Bb 1] N. Bourbaki, "Algèbre Multilinéaire", Algèbre Chapitre 3, Hermann, Paris 1958.

[Bb 2] N. Bourbaki, "Modules Sur Les Anneaux Principaux", Algèbre Chapitre VII, Hermann, Paris 1952.

[Bb 3] N. Bourbaki, "Modules et anneaux semi-simples", Algèbre Chapitre 8, Hermann, Paris 1958.

[Br] R. Brauer, "A note on systems of homogeneous algebraic equations", Bull. A. M. S. 51 (1945), pp. 749-755.

[Bk] J. Browkin, "On forms over p-adic fields", Bull. Acad. Polon. Sci. 14 (1966), pp. 489-492.

[Ca] J.W.S. Cassels, "Diophantine equations with special reference to elliptic curves", J. London Math. Soc. 41 (1966), pp. 193-291.

[C] C. Chevalley, "Démonstration d'une hypothèse de M. Artin", Abh. Math. Sem. Univ. Hamburg vol. 11 (1936), pp. 73-75.

[Co] P.J. Cohen, "Decision procedures for real and p-adic fields", to appear in the N.Y.U. Symposium.

[Da 1] H. Davenport, "Analytic Methods for Diophantine Equations and Diophantine Inequalities", Campus Publishers, Ann Arbor, Mich. 1962.

[Da 2] H. Davenport, "Cubic Forms in 16 Variables", Proc. Royal Soc., Ser. A 272 (1963).

[De] V.B. Demyanov, "On cubic forms over discrete normed fields", Dokl. Akad. Nauk SSSR 74 (1950), pp. 889-891.

[Gb] M.J. Greenberg, "Rational points in Henselian discrete valuation rings", Publ. Math. I.H.E.S. 31 (1967), pp. 59-64.

[Gf] M. Greenleaf, "Irreducible subvarieties and rational points", Am. J. Math. 87 (1965), pp. 25-31.

[K] S. Kochen, "Integer valued rational functions over the p-adic numbers: A p-adic analogue of the theory of real fields", to appear.

[Lg 1] S. Lang, "Introduction to Algebraic Geometry", Interscience, N.Y. (1958).

[Lg 2] S. Lang, "On Quasi Algebraic Closure", Annals of Math. vol. 55 (1952), pp. 373-390.

[Lg 3] S. Lang, "Algebra", Addison-Wesley (1965).

[Lg 4] S. Lang, "The Theory of Real Places", Annals of Math. 57 (1953), pp. 378-391.

[LW] S. Lang and A. Weil, "Number of points of varieties in finite fields", Am. J. Math. 76 (1954), pp. 819-827.

[Lw 1] D.J. Lewis, "Cubic homogeneous polynomials over p-adic fields", Annals of Math. 56 (1952), pp. 473-478.

[Lw 2] D.J. Lewis, "Singular Quartic Forms", Duke Math. J. 21 (1954), pp. 39-44.

[Lu] S. Lubkin, "On a conjecture of A. Weil", Am. J. Math. 89 (1967), pp. 443-548.

[P] L.G. Peck, "Diophantine equations in algebraic number fields", Am. J. Math. 71 (1949), pp. 387-402.

[S] J.-P. Serre, "Corps locaux", Hermann, Paris 1962.

[Ta] A. Tarski, "A decision method for elementary algebra and geometry", 2nd ed., revised, U.C. Press, Berkeley and Los Angeles (1951), 63 pp.

[Te] G. Terjanian, "Un contre-exemple à une conjecture d' Artin", C.R. Acad. Sci. Paris 262 (1966), p. 612.

[Ts] C. Tsen, Divisionsalgebren über Funktionenkörper", Nachr. Ges. Wiss. Göttingen (1933), p. 335.

[Wa] E. Warning, "Bemerkung zur vorstehenden Arbeit von Herrn Chevalley", Abh. Math. Sem. Univ. Hamburg vol. 11 (1936), pp. 76-83.

[We] A. Weil, "Basic Number Theory", Springer Verlag, N.Y. 1967.

[ZS] O. Zariski and P. Samuel, "Commutative Algebra", 2 volumes, Van Nostrand, Princeton 1960.

[Zz 1] B.J. Birch and K. McCann, "A criterion for the p-adic solubility of diophantine equations", Quarterly Journal of Math. 18 (1967), pp. 59-63.

[Zz 2] A. Nerode, "A decision procedure for p-adic integral zeros of diophantine equations", Bull. A. M. S. 69 (1963), pp. 513-17.

INDEX